TERRIFIC SEX
IN FEARFUL TIMES

TERRIFIC SEX
IN FEARFUL TIMES

BROOKS PETERS

ST. MARTIN'S PRESS
New York

LIBRARY OF CONGRESS
Library of Congress Cataloging-in-Publication Data

Peters, Brooks.
Terrific sex in fearful times / by Brooks Peters.
p. cm.
ISBN 0-312-01519-4
1. Sex instruction. 2. Safe sex in AIDS prevention. I. Title.
HQ31.P49 1988
613.9'5—dc19
87-27522
CIP

FIRST EDITION
10 9 8 7 6 5 4 3 2 1

"Voluptuaries of all ages, of every sex, it is to you only that I offer this work; nourish yourselves upon its principles: they favor your passions, and these passions, whereof cold insipid moralists put you in fear, are naught but the means Nature employs to bring man to the ends she prescribes to him; harken only to these delicious promptings, for no voice save that of the passions can conduct you to happiness."

—from *Philosophy in The Bedroom*

A GRATITUDE LIST

Thanks to Charles Spicer, my editor, for his insight and enthusiasm. I would like to express my appreciation to Mathilde Krim, James D'Eramo and my agent, Jed Mattes, for their expertise and encouragement. Special thanks to Jack Heidenry and Philip Nobile for introducing me to the fascinating world of sex research. Adam, Allen, Amy, Beth, Bette, Bill, George, Henry, Jorge, Leonard, Liz, Marina, Michael, Miles, Patrick, Rob, Ronnie, Sam, Stephanie, and Stuart deserve a round of applause. Not to mention the countless other charming, caring people who were kind enough to share their sexiest secrets with me.

AUTHOR'S NOTE

In researching material for this book, I spoke with
many men and women across the country who volun-
teered personal anecdotes and opinions. To ensure
their privacy, I have invented names, personal descriptions and, in some cases, altered quotations, in order
that I may closely reflect, yet subtly disguise who they
are. Any similarity between these characters quoted
within and other living persons is entirely uninten-
tional.

CONTENTS

THE PRELUDE TO TERRIFIC SEX

Contents

THE PRELUDE TO TERRIFIC SEX

INTRODUCTION

PUTTING THE JOY BACK INTO SEX

I love sex.

I think sex is *terrific*.

And I assume since you have taken the time to pick up this book that you do too.

Unfortunately, for many of us, the joy of sex has been overshadowed by the fear of sex. AIDS has dramatically altered the way we, as a society and as individuals, approach making love.

Yet, I can truthfully say that my sex life has never been better.

The threat of disease has caused me to step back and look objectively at what sex means to me personally—physically, emotionally, and psychologically. The process has been difficult, but fascinating. And the rewards have been phenomenal. I used to think about sex in terms of quantity and availability—not quality and selection. I was proud of the number of sexual experiences I had, not necessarily the experiences themselves. Today, I savor sex. It has become a wonderful, positive, essential part of my life.

Along the way I've had to sacrifice some traditionally enjoyable aspects of lovemaking in order to practice today's sensible sex guidelines, but the trade-off has definitely been in my favor. The only thing I've really given up are my inhibitions. But that's the price one pays for Terrific Sex.

It's important for all of us to remember that it isn't sex that causes AIDS, it's a virus. And available to all of us are simple tools of avoiding its exchange. The good news that never makes the headlines is that AIDS is preventable. Indeed, the irony is that by practicing safer sex we can actually halt the spread of the disease.

Safer sex is sex that avoids any contact with bodily fluids, such as sperm, blood, and vaginal secretions. Besides AIDS, of course, there are a number of other sexually transmitted diseases (STDs). Safer sex is also an excellent means of reducing the risk of contracting gonorrhea, syphilis, amoebas, and herpes—not to mention hepatitis. And if you are really careful, you might even be able to prevent that age-old annoying malady—pubic lice, otherwise known as crabs.

With so many advantages, doesn't it make sense to say that in some ways safer sex is better sex?

Terrific Sex in Fearful Times looks at safer sex in detail and shows how you can still have great sex without risking infection. Too many of us think of sex as intercourse leading to orgasm—with all other sexual practices and forms of lovemaking reduced to the heading "foreplay." A young woman I spoke with told me that "unless there is penetration, I don't consider it sex. It's just fooling around." What an unfortunate attitude! It ignores the myriad of erogenous zones of the body and the unlimited erotic potential of the mind.

A thirty-three-year-old actor told me that he stopped having "real sex" two years ago. What, I asked him, is "real sex"? He said, "You know, sex without rubbers." This confused fellow couldn't stop thinking of sex with rubbers as artificial, like having decaffeinated coffee instead of the real thing, or NutraSweet instead of sugar. You can't compare Terrific Sex to products that have had chemicals removed. I prefer to think of sex in terms of how much I can get out of it, not necessarily by how much has been taken away. If the chemistry is there, Terrific Sex will always be *real* sex.

Nor do we have to think of the future of sex in apocalyptic terms. In preparation for this book, I interviewed Dr. Mathilde Krim, founder and co-chair of the American Federation for AIDS Research. Her positive approach to the epidemic has been an inspiration to me. "There are two things I like to say when I talk about AIDS," she told me. "One, it is important to tell young people that this is not forever. Safer sex is an investment in their future. It's quite possible that five years from now we will have drugs to prevent AIDS. True, the virus will remain with humanity forever. But for people who are infected we are going to have drugs that will suppress the multiplication of the virus, hopefully to the point where they will no longer be infectious."

Second, Dr. Krim encourages us to remember that taking precautions in sex is not unique to our generation. "People my age who are sixty or seventy years old today grew up in a time when there were no antibiotics and contraceptives and what we are asking people to do now is what we were doing when we were young. We were extremely careful, I assure you. First of all, because society was less tolerant of pregnancy outside of marriage. And you could die of syphilis. There was no treatment—it was exactly like AIDS. Life was less fun, but we survived. One can adjust. It's a great unpleasantness, but it is not a tragedy. The tragedy is to die. And that, fortunately, can be avoided. There is no reason to live in total fear."

The unexpected by-product of the AIDS threat has been that young people everywhere are reappraising the importance sex has in their lives. The renewed focus has been a process of refinement. Safer sex has opened the door to a new understanding of the joy of sex. Where once we went along with the crowd, succumbing to peer pressure in singles bars and discos, now we are challenging questionable behavior, looking more directly at our needs and desires, rather than relying on other people's expectations. Today we can negotiate the terms of our sex lives. We can insist on having Terrific Sex at all times.

Having undertaken the task of writing a how-to book on sex, it has occurred to me that the reader might well wonder what my qualifications are. First let me state that I am not a zoologist like the noted sex researcher Kinsey. Nor am I a gynecologist like William Masters or a psychologist like his partner Virginia Johnson. I am not a statistician like Shere Hite. In terms of "everything there is to know about sex" I can not give Dr. David Ruben a run for his money. Nor for that matter do I have a leg up on that sensuous woman, "J."

When it comes to sex, I am a complete amateur.

I use the word in its true, original sense, *amator*, the Latin term for lover—a person who engages in an art, science, study, or athletic activity as a pastime rather than as a profession. Since I haven't yet been paid for my talents (I leave that to The Happy Hooker) I continue to enjoy making love for fun, not profit.

Understanding that, I hope you will join me in undertaking this journey—in exploring the incredible world of Terrific Sex. Then you can help me in spreading the word, not the disease.

PART ONE

THE PRELUDE TO TERRIFIC SEX

PRINCIPLE I

THE ADVENTURE OF SEX

Exploring the Terrific Sex Pleasure Principles

Sex. It's probably the most universally known expression on earth. It is very likely the most powerful word in the world. The mere mention of it sends some people into an apoplectic fit of moral outrage. Others get a warm, glowing feeling inside and simply smile. Still others shy away from it out of embarrassment or shame.

From Madison Avenue to Hollywood and Vine and back again to Main Street, U.S.A., sex is our country's favorite topic of conversation. And yet, how infrequently we share our own experience and personal understanding of our erotic natures with others. Even though making love comprises a major portion of our adult lives, we treat it as something too personal, too private, and, all too often, something better left unsaid. As Shere Hite has said, "To discuss sex is to discuss our most basic views of who we are, what we want life to be, and what kind of society we believe in." For many people that's cutting it a little too close for comfort.

Perhaps that's why we've always had a love/hate

3

relationship with sex. From earliest times, the erotic urge has been perceived as "sinful," "depraved," "degrading," "perverse," "evil," "gross," "dirty," and "immoral." Although, certainly, no one has ever called it "dull." Now because of AIDS, sex is increasingly becoming synonymous with death and disease. The Sexual Revolution is losing ground to a rising tide of fear and trepidation. Religious leaders and moralists are happily reminding us that "sex before marriage is wrong." No wonder casual sex has been replaced by uptight sex!

As the eighties come to a close, we're reaching back to time-worn notions of guilt and shame, and returning to former dangerous prejudices. These days we have an even harder time accepting eroticism as a positive, loving, essentially *good* part of life. But if we want sex that is rewarding and pleasurable, we have to rise above our fears and apprehension. We have to shake off these reactionary trappings of moral repugnance and triumph over our ignorance. We have to dispel the myths and unfounded rumors associated with AIDS that continue to incite hysteria and panic, and in some cases, outright cruelty. We have to dare to know the facts that can save our lives and protect others.

It's a tall order, but one that is definitely worth the effort. It requires that we embrace the Three D's— Dedication, Discipline, and most important, Desire. For without the desire for a better future, a healthier body and mind, and the chance to experience a fulfilling and gratifying love life, the promise of *Terrific Sex in Fearful Times* will elude us.

What exactly is Terrific Sex?

Terrific Sex Is Healthy Sex— It stays within the "safer sex" guidelines offered by doctors and experts as a means of AIDS prevention. It's sex that is clean, hygienically speaking, careful, instructive, and ultimately liberating. It is sex without guilt and moral overtones.

Terrific Sex Is Romantic Sex—It's sex between two people who are not afraid of intimacy, of opening up, of being honest with each other. It's sex in which the bodies are totally in tune. It pushes the barriers we ourselves build and unconsciously slave to defend. It breaks down inhibitions and allows us to be who we really are at all times, not just in bed, but at every moment of our lives.

Terrific Sex Is Sensible Sex—It's an approach to eroticism that feels good, yet makes good sense. It is sex that is practical without being predictable. It is dependable, reliable, and responsible lovemaking that allows you to be yourself without playing roles or forcing interests on others. It's sex that is pure and simple and altogether sensational.

Terrific Sex Is Ingenious Sex—It probes the furthest reaches of the imagination for the most provocative, titillating, fascinating methods of making love. It takes advantage of clever tools and novel sex devices for enhancing the physical sensations of sex. It is an erotic approach to life in which we never cease to amaze, to be amazed, to learn, to marvel, to experiment, and to grow.

Terrific Sex Is Beautiful Sex—It lingers lovingly on the aesthetics of the human body, the natural beauty of our muscles and sensuous skin, and the rich rewards of orgasm. It frees the charms of the soul and delights the artistic sensibilities of the mind. It revels in the way a candle sends hot flickers of golden light across a person's scantily clad figure, reclining seductively against soft satin sheets. It is beautiful sex because it is physically attractive, artful sex.

Terrific Sex Is Hot Sex—It gets the juices flowing. It sends shivers up and down your spine. It socks you in the gut and takes your breath away. It makes your arms and legs, your whole body tingle, tremble, shake, rattle and roll! In short, Terrific Sex is sex that blows your mind.

How does one go about achieving this type of extraordinary sex?

That's the question I asked men and women, young and old, rich and poor, gay and straight, black and white, tall and short, extroverted and introverted, from across the country in preparation for this book. It's a question to which I've always sought an answer. The responses I've received over the years have helped me to formulate a series of fifteen steps called the Terrific Sex Pleasure Principles which are virtually guaranteed to change the way you think about sex. They are as follows:

THE TERRIFIC SEX PLEASURE PRINCIPLES

1. Approach sex as an adventure—a positive, joyful, thrilling part of life.
2. Follow the Terrific Sex risk-reducing guidelines. Face the facts regarding AIDS and take appropriate preventive measures.
3. Discover the Sheer Pleasure of Condoms. Acquaint yourself with the ins and outs, the pluses and minuses, the pros and cons of proper prophylactic use.
4. Study the anatomy of a Sex Star—yourself! Educate the senses with self-awareness exercises, and body exploration.
5. Hone your sexual skills by learning the secrets of Sexercise! Stay fit, eat right, and reduce stress.
6. Uncover your true erotic personality by writing your very own Sex Bio.
7. Design a Terrific Sex Plan to improve your romantic life, deciding when, where, how and with whom you make love.
8. Master the Sensual Arts of Kissing, Massage and Full-Body Frottage.
9. Expose yourself to the delights of Good Clean Fun—Sexy Showers, Steamy Baths and Hot Lights!
10. Improve your sexual prowess by discovering and practicing the Art of Solo Sex.

11. Double your pleasure by learning the merits of Mutual Masturbation. Keep your partner happy with new and exotic methods of duo-eroticism.
12. Develop a taste for Safe Oral Sex. Master the latest techniques of risk-free cunnilingus and fellatio.
13. Experience the thrills of the Fearless Fuck. Unlock the super-lover inside of yourself.
14. Revel in the charms of Romance. Find out how you can create the perfect erotic atmosphere.
15. Take a trip into the compelling world of Sexual Fantasy. Unleash the potential for Terrific Sex found in Erotica, Phone Sex and Lite S&M.

Coining the expression "the pleasure principle," Freud stated that "it seems our entire psychical activity is bent upon procuring pleasure and avoiding pain . . . Consideration of the most intense pleasure of which man is capable, the pleasure in the performance of the sexual act leaves little doubt upon this point." If the avoidance of fear can be compared to the avoidance of pain, then couldn't the idea of a "pleasure principle" be applied to alleviating the anxiety associated with AIDS that has imbued the sexual act with an unprecedented amount of fear? Couldn't safer sex be the key to restoring our ability to enjoy making love fearlessly?

The answer, happily, is yes. I've been able to turn my life around by practicing these "pleasure principles." So have many of the men and women whom I interviewed and who shared their passionate sexual secrets with me. The exciting truth is that the Terrific Sex Pleasure Principles can open the door to a wonderful world of sexual satisfaction and joy for anyone. All

you have to do is take the initiative—the first step—
and you'll be on your way.

Guess what? You already have! Just by reading
this far. It's obvious you look upon love, romance, and
sex as adventures of the spirit or you wouldn't have
set out on this journey.

At first reading, the Pleasure Principles might
seem like a long hard climb. But believe me, once you
get started, you won't want to turn back.

PRINCIPLE 2

SEX IN THE AIDS ERA

The Bare Facts

Erich Fromm stated in *The Art of Loving* that the "practice of love requires discipline." Little did he know that his words would have a double meaning in the age of AIDS. Now more than ever it is crucial that a sexually active person face the sobering facts regarding this serious, fatal disease.

What has shocked me most about this health crisis is how much misinformation exists regarding how AIDS is transmitted, and who is at risk of contracting it.

WHAT, ME WORRY?

The naked truth is anyone can get AIDS.

While technically speaking, AIDS is very hard to get (casual contact has been ruled out as a means of transmission, including toilet seats, doorknobs, touching, sweat, shaking hands, and light kissing), the simple truth is you can get AIDS whether you're gay or straight, married or single, man or woman, young or old, chaste or promiscuous. As a poster distributed by the AIDS Hotline in New York stipulates, "AIDS does not discriminate."

According to recent estimates put forth by the Atlanta Centers for Disease Control 1.5 to 2 million Americans have already been exposed to the AIDS virus. The number will most likely increase dramatically in the next few years. Federal scientists project that by the end of 1991, the total number of cases will reach 270,000 with 179,000 deaths unless better treatments are found. Four to seven percent of those infected will have become infected through heterosexual intercourse. At present, heterosexuals represent the smallest number of cases, but in terms of percentages, they are the fastest growing risk group.

AIDS is increasingly spreading to women. In New York City alone, AIDS is the leading killer of women between the ages of 25 to 34. In America, seven percent of people with AIDS are women. That figure is likely to grow. Hundreds of women have given birth to babies infected with the virus. The disease is affecting the lives of women from all communities, through their families, their friends, and ultimately through their fears.

I have encountered a surprising amount of resistance from some young people in compiling this book. A large number of them think that AIDS does not affect them; that the threat is being exaggerated by the media which, they argue, are more interested in profits than in people. One young man told me that he was sure the threat was minor. "I think quite honestly," he said, "that it is a carefully engineered media hype that the gay community has invented to scare the heterosexual population into being more concerned for their plight." While I can't argue with the fact that the gay community is avidly seeking assistance and is taking extraordinary measures to achieve it, it is ridiculous to downplay the danger the disease poses to all of us.

Dr. Mathilde Krim points out that "the risk is very real. The size of the threat varies depending on where you live and what your lifestyle is. For a woman who is unattached and sexually active, and who lives in New York (and there are many of those) and who has one or two or three or four or more friends a year, which is quite normal, the risk is very real. It can be calculated. Taking the figures of the Health Department, that there are a half-million people infected in New York alone, and assuming that half of them are exclusively gay men, that leaves a quarter of a million infected. Even assuming that some of them are women, it boils down to 150,000 males who are heterosexual (predominantly, or partially, it doesn't matter). Even assuming that 50,000 of these men are real bums and no respectable girl would have anything to do with them, that nevertheless leaves a pool of 50,000 to 100,000 eligible infected bachelors in this town. It is quite possible that a woman might meet such a man in very respectable circumstances and develop an affection for him. And how many men, total, does she have to choose from? The upper limit would be one million. So for New York City, the statistics are one in ten, or one in twenty."

The same kind of deductive reasoning can be applied to any major city in the country. The numbers might be different, but the reality of the threat is in no way diminished.

So the answer to the question, "What, me worry?" is a very loud, unqualified "Yes!"

By all means, take the trouble to be informed. Be aware of the threat of the disease. Take the necessary precautions as outlined in this and other books. You will thereby reduce your level of anxiety and help prevent its exchange.

THE TERRIFIC SEX GROUND RULES

In contemplating the threat of AIDS, as it affects one's sexual behavior, there are five essential ground rules that bear repeating. Keep them in the back of your mind at all times, like mantras of proper sexual hygiene. These slogans can help you, no matter what risk group you fall into, and even if you don't fall into any risk group.

1) It's Not Who You Are, but What You Do.

You are ultimately responsible for your health. Make sure your behavior lives up to your attitudes. Talking a good line isn't going to protect you unless you follow it up by your behavior in the bedroom.

2) ABC—Always Be Careful!

The ABCs are the building blocks to sensible sex. Don't let your passions overwhelm your common sense. No thrill is worth forsaking your pledge to practice safer sex.

3) When in Doubt, Check It Out.

The moment you think something or someone is out of line—whether it's before, during, or after sex—stop, look and investigate. Don't be lazy, or timid. Take the initiative before it's too late.

4) Out of Body, Out of Mind.

Make sure that any ejaculations occur outside the body—never inside. Think of the penis as a large needle that can shoot the virus into your bloodstream during sex. As always, the best projection is no injection.

5) K.I.S.S.—Keep It Sexy, but Simple.

The more complicated sex is, the more difficult it will be to maintain safeguards. While your sexual fantasies can be as Byzantine as you wish, it is suggested you don't try to juggle too many sexual activities at one time. This holds true especially in terms of multiple sex partners. The more variables, the harder it is for you to manage a healthy routine.

THE BOTTOM LINE

All of these safer sex guidelines boil down to one major consideration. *Don't exchange any body fluids.*

Let's look at the list of the riskiest ones:

BLOOD
SEMEN
PRE-SEMINAL FLUID
VAGINAL SECRETIONS

(NOTE: The virus has also been located in SALIVA and TEARS, but experts do not consider these high risk. Other bodily emissions to be cautious of are URINE, FECES and BREAST MILK. It is best to avoid any contact with these substances, especially during sex, since the risk factor is there. We'll be talking more specifically about SALIVA in the upcoming chapter on kissing.)

As for the primary high-risk fluids listed above, let's be more particular about each one to illustrate how and why these bodily secretions are considered dangerous.

Blood

You can contract AIDS by letting someone else pass the HIV virus to you through their blood. For example, when drug users share a needle, a little bit of blood is passed along on the tip of the needle and in the syringe. That is why drug use is the second-most common means of transmission. Don't share needles!

Likewise, when you receive a blood transfusion, there is a chance you might be infected. Now that the AIDS test is being used to screen donations, this risk has been greatly reduced. But it is one of the methods through which people have been exposed in the past, and it underscores the importance blood plays in transmitting this disease. By the way, there is no danger to yourself in giving blood.

In terms of sex, blood is a likely candidate for transmission, because blood is often present during intercourse. During the act of coitus, tiny tears can be formed in the lining of the vagina (and most notably in the case of anal intercourse, inside the rectum). Normally these breaks are of little consequence, but because of AIDS they are now extremely relevant. The virus is apt to pass through (via semen) into these tiny openings and enter the bloodstream. Less likely, but still possible, the virus can be spread from the blood released inside the vagina onto the porous skin of the penis, especially if the penis is chafed and the skin has been broken, or if an open sore is present. For this reason, syphilis is considered a dangerous cofactor in AIDS transmission—a good reason to have a full medical examination before you engage in sex with someone you don't know. Either way, the chance of infection can be greatly diminished by using a prophylactic. This will also be covered in greater detail in the upcoming chapter "The Sheer Pleasure of Condoms."

It is recommended that you don't have sex that is coarse or forceful. Avoid inserting large objects, including your hand, into the vagina or anus, which may tear the inner linings, or the orifices themselves.

There are a number of ways you could come into

contact with a person's blood during oral sex. If previous sex play has been rough, or if the woman is menstruating, the risk is clear. Biting and scratching should be avoided as well.

Semen

Semen has metaphorically been referred to as "white blood" and for this reason you can see why any sexual contact with this fluid is a risk factor in the transmission of AIDS. Semen is the milky white substance that is secreted by the prostate gland and the seminal vesicle in the male. During orgasm, it transports the millions of sperm ejaculated out of the testes. The exchange of semen into the bloodstream can occur during vaginal intercourse, anal intercourse, and oral intercourse. It can also theoretically take place if you ejaculate directly onto an open cut or sore of a person's skin. Otherwise, the skin is considered a remarkably safe and effective protective shield. Hence the slogan used by the Gay Men's Health Crisis, "On Me, Not In Me" in reference to ejaculation.

Pre-Seminal Fluid

Secreted by the Cowper's glands in men, pre-seminal fluid (also known as pre-cum or pre-ejaculatory fluid) is the viscous, often clear liquid that seeps out of the penis prior to ejaculation. The AIDS virus has been found in pre-seminal fluid, but there is no evidence that any one case has been caused by it directly. Until all the facts are available, it is wiser to avoid vaginal, anal, and oral contact with this substance.

Contrary to popular opinion, and in spite of its

nickname, pre-cum can form at any time during sexual arousal, not just before orgasm. Even if you think you haven't secreted any pre-seminal fluid, don't be so sure it isn't there. Remember these fluids are often indistinguishable from sweat, moisture, and any lubricant you might be using. Plus, sperm itself is microscopic and traces of it might be found in the pre-seminal liquid. In the past women have gotten pregnant on the misconception that pre-cum doesn't contain any sperm. Quite often it does, either as a residue from a previous ejaculation, or because of current smaller emissions. These past mistakes should serve as a warning and as a guide to those experimenting with oral sex without rubbers. The risk is real. Mind your ABCs!

Vaginal Secretions

Vaginal secretions serve to lubricate the vagina and the labia minora at the first signs of sexual arousal. These fluids are emitted from the vaginal lining much the way that sweat beads on one's brow. Traces of the AIDS virus have been found in this fluid as well, and so it is considered a factor in the transmission of the disease from women to men. Care should be taken during cunnilingus and vaginal intercourse that these vital fluids don't enter the bloodstream either through the mouth or the penis. Proper protection in both sexual activities would necessitate the use of prophylactics or a latex sheet during oral sex.

DENIAL

Denial is one of the most insidious aspects of the AIDS disease. Today it is not bad luck that is going to get you. It's denial.

Having spoken with numerous people, I am constantly coming face to face with it in writing this book. One young woman told me she was protected because she had an exceptionally resilient immune system. She didn't understand that although this is a bonus, it is not a carte blanche to go out and have indiscriminate sex. Besides, one can be a carrier without having any symptoms. One young man told me he was spiritually protected. And a college-educated woman confided to me that she could "just tell" whether someone was infected or at risk. She trusted her instincts. Unfortunately, the AIDS virus doesn't care about your instincts or intuition. It is an opportunistic parasite that thrives on people's ignorance. Before it infiltrates your immune system, AIDS first attacks your denial system.

THE AIDS TEST

No issue has caused as much controversy as the so-called AIDS Test—a blood test that tells you whether you have antibodies to the AIDS virus in your blood.

The presence of the antibodies indicates that you have been exposed to the disease. Should you take it?

My advice is one of caution. Talk it over with your doctor and family and friends before making up your mind. The test results can only help you if the news is good. If they aren't, you might suffer depression. Either way you should be practicing safer sex, so, in a certain sense, the test results are irrelevant. The attitude of one woman I interviewed underscores the problem inherent in the AIDS test. When asked if she practices safer sex, she said, "Sure, I took the AIDS test and I'm safe." This is not a logical conclusion to make. You mustn't use the AIDS test as a method of safe sex, the way some people look upon abortion as a means of birth control. The information is useless unless you take the appropriate actions sexually. As Dr. Krim points out, "the AIDS test alone doesn't protect you at all."

Protection is the key. "A negative test," Dr. Krim continues, "does not mean being free of the virus. You might have acquired the virus and not had time to develop the antibodies. If you want to be really sure, and even that is not absolute certainty, but if you want to increase the degree of reliability of the negative test results, you have to wait at least three months, during which you don't incur any risk at all, which means, strictly speaking, that you have to be abstinent sexually. Then you take the test a second time. But even so we know from the medical literature that some people don't develop the antibody for one year after infection. Four percent of them. It is startling. The negative result is never absolute certainty. A new partner is somebody someone should relate to through the practice of safer sex. No matter what the test says."

COPING WITH FEAR

Some of the most disconcerting by-products of the AIDS epidemic are the panic and hysteria that accompany it. Because of fear a large percentage of the population can be characterized as "the worried well." AIDS anxiety has become so acute that some people have actually committed suicide. Writing in her remarkable book, *Illness As Metaphor*, Susan Sontag argues that "any disease that is treated as a mystery and acutely enough feared will be felt to be morally, if not literally, contagious." Sontag's warning has special relevance to the current epidemic.

A woman I spoke with worried that "we're getting to the point now where just to walk out on the street, you're going to have to step into a condom and pull it over your head." Fortunately, this state of affairs has not come to pass.

AIDS fear can come upon you suddenly or be a persistent condition. The solution is to share your thoughts about it with friends and family, doctors and therapists. Get as much medical information about yourself as possible. Go to the doctor and get a full physical.

"Stacy" is a young, vivacious cabaret singer. She went through a period when she couldn't stop thinking about AIDS. "Those epidemiologists screaming out those charts and graphs scared me to death," she relates. "I couldn't even kiss somebody without thinking about death. Even the smartest person can't help being infiltrated by it. There is a shadow. I know people who

21

think about AIDS all the time, and I worry about them because they use it as a way of punishing themselves." Stacy finds herself worried a lot of the time, too, mostly because she has slept with a lot of gay and bisexual men. "Being a part of the theatre world, I found myself falling in love with an awful lot of gay guys. I don't think if I worked at Citibank, I would be so scared. When friends of mine started to get sick, I looked at my swollen glands. As a singer, I always have swollen glands. And the fact that I smoke a lot doesn't help. Anyway, I called the Gay Men's Health Crisis hotline and I think they were a little surprised to hear from me. I know it's for gay men, but I'm in contact with a lot of gay men. A stiff talk with them cleared my mind a lot. I was suddenly talking to people who were talking to people who had it." (As a matter of fact, the GMHC does a great deal of work with women, as does the group Women At Risk.)

"Veronica," an attractive television producer, opted to take the AIDS test to alleviate her extreme fears after consulting with a doctor. She had slept with someone later diagnosed as having ARC (AIDS-Related Complex) and was concerned that it might have an effect on her current monogamous relationship. "I found a doctor I could trust through my cousin. He had a good reputation. I wanted one who would do it anonymously. I didn't want to be on a list of names of antibody-positive people. People seem to forget that Auschwitz was only a little more than forty years ago. It was a very clandestine affair. I had to walk the blood tests over to the lab myself."

Veronica felt comfortable in discussing the nature of her sex life with this doctor. "When I met him, he was quite surprised to see me. I saw his eyebrows go up when I walked in with my very corporate haircut, my Brooks Brothers suit, my string of pearls, and my alligator purse. He said, 'What are you doing here?' And I replied that I just found out someone I slept with has ARC. He seemed surprised, and then said, 'Well, you belong here.' I had a lot of anxiety about doing it, but this doctor made it a very compassionate experience. Still, it was a horrible time for me. I couldn't rid myself of the anxiety. Dawn was the worst. I would wake up and open my eyes and be filled with this impending sense of doom. It didn't seem fair. I felt like I was morally paying for having once enjoyed sex."

Luckily, for Veronica, the results came back negative. Although test results are not one hundred percent accurate, she was greatly reassured. But she understands that her fears will only return unless she continues to practice safer sex.

Another example of how AIDS anxiety can creep up on you is the story of "Charles," a thirty-year-old waiter from Boston. Prior to the health crisis, Charles led a sexually active life. He slept around with a great number of men and women. But when the news came out that there was a disease going around that could kill, Charles changed his ways and stopped having casual, anonymous sex. Now, four years later, he's still scared. He hasn't taken the AIDS Test because in his case his doctor recommends against it. Instead, he is extra careful to work out in the gym everyday, eat properly, practice safer sex, and sleep regularly. He feels fine, but underneath his healthy facade, he is terrified that he is going to die from AIDS. A number of his friends already have.

One afternoon while showering at the gym, Charles noticed a small purple mark on his stomach. His first thought was Kaposi's sarcoma, the cancer that is associated with AIDS. He didn't panic immediately. But his mood switched from feeling good about himself to utter self-loathing and self-pity. "Oh, shit, I thought," he relates, "I've got AIDS. What else could that purple mark be. Later, as I was drying off, I tried to calm myself down by repeating over and over again that I was simply overreacting. When friends called during the next couple of hours, I could hardly talk to them. My life flashed before my eyes and all I could think about was my will, my job, and my family. Life seemed too short. At one point, I cried."

A few days went by. The mark was still there. Charles finally broke down and went to see his doctor. At first the doctor couldn't figure out what the strange purple mark was, but one thing was sure, he said, "It isn't Kaposi's sarcoma." Greatly relieved, Charles left the doctor and returned to his daily routine. For the price of a doctor's visit, he had his peace of mind back. Back at the gym, he showed the purple mark to his weight trainer and jokingly related that he had thought he was going to die. The trainer laughed and pointed to a similar purple mark on his own stomach. " 'The mark comes from a burst capillary,' " he told me— " 'from working out too hard!' "

The moral of this story: Go easy on yourself. Get all the facts before you worry yourself sick. Don't let your fears and imagination get the better of you.

DRUGS AND YOU

According to *The New York Times*, "The overwhelming majority of the AIDS cases attributed to heterosexual transmission so far have been caused by intravenous drug users, especially in the Northeast." This has severe consequences for those people engaged in sexual relationships with drug users. According to state drug officials, almost ninety percent of the cases in New York City attributed to heterosexual contact have involved the sex partners of intravenous drug users.

If you are dating or living with an IV drug user, make sure you practice safer sex at all times. Try and help your friend to recognize his or her problem, and to stop using drugs. You will need to seek assistance— you can't do it alone. But remember that you have to put your health first.

If you are using drugs, be apprised that there are risk factors in drugs besides IV use. Not only do you run the risk of infection from a contaminated needle, but your repeated drug intake actually interferes with your immune system's ability to function properly. Speed, cocaine, crack, alcohol, marijuana, and all other toxic substances (including diet pills) can impair your immune system. To a lesser degree, this goes for cigarettes and coffee too. Repeated harmful exposure to the sun can also affect your immune system.

Now that we've covered the bare essentials of AIDS prevention, having learned the fundamental truths regarding the transmission of the HIV virus, and how we can best overcome our fears, let's move on to Principle 3, in which we discover the Sheer Pleasure of Condoms. Here we can devote our full attention to one of mankind's most popular inventions. This simple, straightforward latex sleeve opens the door to an astonishing array of erotic opportunities.

While we'll be covering the specifics on how to enjoy Terrific Sex in much more explicit detail later on—in particular the joys of fearless intercourse and oral sex—it's imperative that we have a working knowledge and understanding of what a condom is and how it functions in safer sex before we can begin to explore the other Pleasure Principles with confidence and just the right amount of *savoir-faire*.

PRINCIPLE 3

THE SHEER PLEASURE OF CONDOMS

A BRIEF HISTORY

According to Kit Schwartz (author of the *The Male Member: Being A Compendium Of Facts, Figures, Foibles and Anecdotes about the Loving Organ*, St. Martin's Press), the oldest example of a condom appears in a cave painting found in the south of France, dating back to 15,000 B.C. Anthropologists assume the first prophylactics were sheaths made out of animal hide designed to protect the caveman's genitals from exposure to the sun and to the cold, as well as the curious insect or rodent. Schwartz documents that in ancient Egypt sturdy sleeves were worn as protection during battle, while thinner covers were worn daily to protect against tropical skin diseases. "Some sheaths," she writes, "were adorned with jewels to define social status." In the East, others were carved from horn, ivory, or wood, or fashioned from tin, lead, copper, or even iron.

Not only mortals were in need of protection. The Roman author Antoninus Liberalis described the Greek demi-god Minos as wearing a "goat's membrane" around his penis because his sperm was "infested with serpents and scorpions."

Gabriel Fallopius, who made a name for himself as the discoverer of the fallopian tubes, took time out from his studies of female anatomy to devote his attentions to the problems of venereal disease. He designed a simple "linen cloth made to fit over the glans" that helped prevent infection during intercourse. According to him, in his book *De Morbo Gallico*, he "tried this experiment on eleven hundred men, and I call immortal God to witness not one of them was infected." Goodness, gracious, that's a lot of linen!

It was left to the possibly apocryphal personage of "Colonel Condom," an English army physician to Charles II, to finally invent the modern-day equivalent of the condom. The device, made of intestinal skin, was secured at the tip with a little ribbon. Shaking off their own inventiveness, the British have always claimed the French devised the rubber, calling it the French Letter. The French responded in kind by naming it the English Overcoat.

Other euphemisms for the "glove that dare not speak its name" include the armor, the safety cap, the potent ally, the bag, the cabinet of love, the preserver, the shield, the amoral guise, the safety sheath, the machine, and the never-failing engine. The Marquis de Sade called it "a little sack of Venetian skin." A curious irony is that in *Troilus And Cressida* Hector says to Menelaus regarding his wife that she "swears still by Venus' glove"—a Shakespearean euphemism for a condom. The woman in question was none other than Helen of Troy—indisputably, the reigning expert on Trojans.

During the First World War, condom use became more prevalent. Yankee soldiers, coming home from overseas, returned with knowledge of contraceptives as VD prevention devices. As time marched on, improvements were made. Condoms became lubricated, spermicided, ribbed, stippled, and built with reservoir ends to catch the ejaculated sperm. Now they come flavored (for oral sex), colored (in a variety of shocking hues), built for smaller men ("Snuggers"), as well as those still made from lamb's skin for more discriminating tastes.

While lamb's skin condoms can run you as much as three times more than the regular latex rubber, many men find them much more appealing since they are natural and super sensitive. Others claim that they are less constricting and less numbing. Fourex, produced by Schmid Laboratories (who also make the latex bestseller, Sheik) has been around since 1888. The Fourex condom is made from a part of a lamb's intestine called the caecum. Apparently, it takes one whole New Zealand lamb to make one skin sheath. No wonder it costs more than the latex version.

In terms of Terrific Sex, however, keep in mind that the latest findings in condom research indicate that lamb's skin prophylactics are not as risk-free as latex and rubber ones because the naturally porous skin could allow the AIDS virus to get through. You're better safe than sorry—so for our purposes, it's best not to use them.

Perhaps the most innovative development in the history of condoms is the marketing of them to women. The female market now constitutes over half of all sales. Finding themselves in the predicament of having to rely on their own methods of contraception, and troubled by the potential side-effects of the Pill, many women have chosen to buy condoms on their own, insisting that their husbands, boyfriends, and lovers use them. Even concerned mothers have been known to give them to their growing sons. As "Alene," a flight attendant, told me, "Most guys will wear them if it's a choice of using one or not having sex."

Now because of AIDS, women have yet another reason to look out for themselves—and condom manufacturers have come up with condoms specifically geared to a female market. One brand, the Mentor line, costs a lot more than an equivalent condom for the male market. But it comes with an applicator that allows you to put on the condom without ever having to touch it. It also comes equipped with a special adhesive lubricant that secures the condom to the penis. The Lady Protex line comes in two varieties, lubricated with spermicide (the blue and silver package) and lubricated "ultra-thin" (pink and silver).

Up until the AIDS crisis, homosexual men were proud of the fact that they didn't have to bother with rubbers. The issue of contraception was irrelevant. A condom always, however, came in handy as a reliable protection against venereal disease. Then came AIDS—and a dramatic upsurge in the use of condoms by gay men. At first, it was hard for homosexuals to adjust to the idea of having to sport a "skin" just like their straight counterparts. Being gay was losing some of its fringe benefits. But eventually the idea caught on—out of necessity—and profit-minded entrepreneurs once again took advantage of a developing market. National Sanitary Labs designed a prophylactic called "Man Form Plus" that was more lubricated than the normal rubber, to assist in anal sex. In 1982, Doc Johnson Enterprises began manufacturing a brand called MAN TO MAN. Their latest product, MAN TO MAN Plus, is supposed to be stronger, while HUNKY DUDES is extra-thin. Now they're marketing a brand called ULTIMATE which comes with the spermicide Nonoxynol-9 and is being packaged for both straight and gay markets.

Please note, however, that the Centers for Disease Control in Atlanta refuse to endorse the use of Nonoxynol-9 as a means of killing off the HIV virus. It has not yet been fully proven to be a completely reliable means of AIDS prevention. There is certainly no harm in using it as an extra safeguard in proper safer sex technique.

HOW SAFE ARE CONDOMS?

Condoms have to be approved by stringent Food and Drug Administration standards of quality and strength. A typical prophylactic must withstand 4000 pounds of pressure per square inch before being approved. According to a report in The New York Times, a spokesman for the Food and Drug Administration claimed that close to twenty percent of condoms tested for water-leakage during a four-month period had a failure rate that exceeded agency standards. The failure rate, the article noted, "was significantly higher among imported brands than domestic brands." Nevertheless, the agency is allowing latex condom manufacturers to advertise their products as helpful in the prevention of AIDS as long as they stipulate that the assertions "reflect accurately the realistic expectations a consumer should have about the condom's effectiveness."

THE PRELUDE TO TERRIFIC SEX

This is an excellent point. A condom is only as good as the person using it. Even with the surprising 20 percent failure rate of the sample tested, a condom's potential for leaking will have no bearing on one's sexual encounter if the practice of ejaculating outside the body is maintained at all times. Rubbers should be thought of as a tool of safer sex—not a guarantee or fool-proof insurance policy. Keep in mind that condoms are not made of steel. They can tear, slip and be misused. Beware of long fingernails and overly calloused hands. And most important, don't use oil-based lubricants because the condom will disintegrate when exposed to oil. Avoid Vaseline and other petroleum jellies. Stick to water soluble lubes such as KY Jelly.

"Craig," a very handsome thirty-two-year-old Hollywood screenwriter, told this story about a condom experience he had with a girlfriend he met at a convention. "Everything was perfect. We went out to dinner, talked forever, and finally ended up back at her hotel room. We made out for a long time. She asked me if I wanted to fuck her and I said, 'Of course, I do, but I didn't bring a rubber.' She laughed and told me she had her own. Indeed she did. I slipped one on and tried to enter her, but the condom was unlubricated and she was too dry. Anxious to get the ball rolling, I grabbed a jar of Vaseline that I saw on the side of her night table and rubbed some on the head of my cock. I slipped right in, and we made fast furious love. It felt so great inside her. Like I wasn't wearing a condom at all. We both came together and for a moment I thought this had been one of the best nights of my life because I was enjoying safe sex so much. Here I was coming inside her without any risk of getting her pregnant or of contracting some disease. Or so I thought. When I pulled out I couldn't believe my eyes. There was no condom left on my cock, except the ring around the base. It had completely disintegrated and I had come inside her after all. I was very shaken, totally upset. I started trembling and worrying. I told her to go in the bathroom and wash herself out. When I had a chance I washed my cock with soap and water. Then I doused it with hydrogen peroxide that I found in the medicine cabinet. Afterwards, we were both so nervous we could hardly talk to each other. I wish I'd known that Vaseline would have such an effect. But no one had ever mentioned it before."

Well, now we're mentioning it. Please be careful.

The problems that arise in condom use are exacerbated when it comes to anal sex. Here it is doubly important that you practice the safer sex guidelines to the letter. Always ejaculate outside the body. The risk of infection during anal sex is considered quantitatively higher since the lack of natural lubrication can result in tearing of the sensitive rectal linings, as well as the condom itself. Some gay men advocate using two condoms—"double-bagging it." Anyone, gay or straight, who enjoys this sexual activity should maintain the utmost care to avoid exchanging the virus by accident.

Regarding fellatio, prophylactics offer a sensible solution to a problematic issue. As I explain in further detail in the upcoming chapter "Delights Down Under—How to Enjoy Safe Oral Sex," a condom allows for greater freedom and flexibility in practicing fellatio.

Recent reports regarding prostitutes claim that most of them are now using condoms when performing oral sex. It's even been stated that some hookers know how to apply a condom with their mouths so that they can slip it onto a john's penis without him even noticing. Now that's a trick that demonstrates a great deal of oral dexterity. I can't think of any reason why you shouldn't try it yourself. Once you get past the alkaline coating (you can wipe it off with a washcloth), the rubber actually tastes pretty good.

SUPPLY & DEMAND

In the age of AIDS, it is a wise choice to have a condom with you or near you at all times. You may wish to store a couple in your car, or in your kit bag. Contrary to popular habit, don't keep a stash in your wallet. They tend to dry out and become unreliable. If you have a white collar job, keep a few in your attaché case, or in your suit pockets. If you're a jock, keep one in your gym bag. You probably won't need the condom while you're working out, but if you plan on meeting someone after leaving the gym, it's best to be prepared. Also, if you maintain a second home, or a vacation residence, you'll want to keep a stash there. If you're snowed in, or sick, you'll always have what you need.

Con-Pac, Inc. has concocted a clever device called the Con-Pac Condom Case, "The safe, discreet way to carry condoms." This handsome item comes in silver or gold plate with a brushed finish, and is designed to hold two standard-size packaged condoms. And it snaps securely closed for your convenience. As the ad campaign stipulates, "It's the safe sex gift that says you care."

Keep in mind that condoms can dry out if stored near heat. Look at the package. See the date of issue. This is not an expiration date like you would find on a

milk carton. This is the date the condom was packaged. Manufacturers recommend not using a condom
if it's more than two years old.

CONDOM SENSE

How do you bring up the subject of using condoms?
We'll cover that more completely in the upcoming section regarding Safe Sex Negotiation, but for now let's
look at what happens in the bedroom just as the man
is about to put the condom on.

Let's say you're in bed together and it's time to
talk condoms. You're nervous. If you're a woman, you
may be embarrassed that you're taking such an active
role in discussing sex. A lot of women have told me
that they're afraid to talk about sex in bed. Beth Bro-
derick, co-director of the AIDS Outreach Program at
St. Peter's Church in New York City, told me "women
are not supposed to appear to be sexually knowledgeable, so it's very hard for them to suddenly whip out a
condom and say, 'Hey, put this on.' But the whole
world is going to have to grow up. We can't afford this
type of double standard anymore. We have a real duty
to ourselves to explore our sexuality. Not only to explore it, but to promote it as well."

If you're a man, you may be worried that bringing
up the subject will disrupt the mood your partner is in.
Quite the contrary. She's going to interpret your reti-
cence as disinterest. So speak up. Get over the initial

embarrassment and broach the subject. If you have to, snap your fingers and say, "I think it's time I put on a rubber." Or try the subtle approach. "I'll be back in a second with a little surprise." Clearly, the way you handle it depends on your relationship, how long you've known each other, how much sex you've had together, and also how comfortable you are just talking about sex.

Once you've got the rubber in your hands (always have more than one with you in case one breaks), keep the talk going. Tell her how pretty she looks lying there looking at you. Make scrumptious sexual overtures with your eyes or your mouth. Kiss her while you're unraveling the sterile package. Try to lighten up the atmosphere. You may wish to let her feel the sexy texture of the stretchy material. Unravel it completely, letting her see what it looks like undone. This will help reduce the tension and discomfort and take the mystery out of it. Grab it by both ends and stretch! See how expansive it gets. Indeed a condom can expand to six feet or more if blown up. You could even slip it over your head and rob a bank if you wanted to. But for now, try a different exercise. Take the rubber and stretch it over your fingers (or hers), as if it were a latex glove. Cover the entire hand with it, pulling down over the fist, down to the wrist. Believe it or not, the condom will fit without breaking or tearing (unless your fingernails are extra-long, and/or sharp.) See how extraordinarily flexible and durable a condom is! Now you can see that if a condom is used properly there is no reason to fear it will break. It is generally when a condom hasn't been stored properly, is incorrectly lubricated, or is mishandled that problems of breakage arise.

Once you're both comfortable with the prophylactic, it's time to get down to business. Slip the circle around the head of your penis and gently roll it down the length of your shaft. Ask her to help you.

Occasionally, putting on a rubber can have its difficulties:

a) Sometimes the rubber is too tight. If you have a penis that is extra-thick, having stretched the condom on your hand first will help. Or ask your pharmacist for those condoms designed for men who are more endowed.

b) Be careful not to get any pubic hairs caught in the latex as you're pulling it down. This can make even the toughest stud wince. Sometimes you're going to have to lose a few hairs. Don't worry, they'll grow back soon enough. *The Joy Of Sex* recommends that you prune your pubic hair before slipping on a condom. Or shave the whole area.

c) If your penis is small and the rubber is too flimsy a cover, you may wish to secure it on the bottom, but preferably you'll find a product that fits your needs.

d) If during the putting on phase you find that too much time is passing, try not to get nervous. Relax, breathe out and, if you want, ask your partner to assist you. This will not only relieve the pressure, it could also be an exciting bit of foreplay. If she's a curious person, she'll be just as eager as you to see how the condom works. If she's smart, she'll be double checking to see that it fits properly and hasn't already torn.

e) If you lose your erection, don't become discouraged. It happens all the time. Put the condom aside for a moment and go back to kissing and foreplay. Pretty soon, things should start perking up.

f) Sometimes it's hard to tell which side is the right side to put a condom on. If it's lubricated you can usually tell because the lubricated side is designed to go on the outside to help you ease inside the vagina.

I've heard stories of men who've put these on backwards and find the lubrication feels fantastic, but this way the prophylactic has a greater chance of slipping off.

Some condoms come with nozzles at the end that are reservoirs for the ejaculate. These are recommended because a rubber can burst if you ejaculate into it and there is no room inside for the sperm to escape. They also greatly enhance the sensation of ejaculating since the emission of sperm is not interfered with at the opening, or meatus, of the urethra.

AT YOUR DISPOSAL

Removing the condom after sex does not have to be a secret, hushed, embarrassing act either. First make sure as you withdraw from the vagina that you hold onto the very base of your penis where the bottom of the condom is. This will help make sure that the sheath won't slide off as you pull out. Then carefully remove the rubber, taking care not to spill any of the ejaculate. You can do whatever you want with it after that, tying it into a knot and flinging it over your shoulder or throwing it into the fireplace. Go for a jump shot into the wastepaper basket. But plumbers have pleaded that you don't flush rubbers down the toilet. They can fill with water, expand and cause drainage problems in the sewage system. Your best bet is to wrap it in a tissue and throw it away.

Just because you came inside a prophylactic does not mean that you are now free to put your penis back inside your partner. This is a mistake in judgment that has caused plenty of women a lot of grief since they've gotten pregnant from such ignorance. If you want to have intercourse or oral sex again, make sure you wash the penis thoroughly and put on another rubber. One final note—never use the same condom more than once.

PRINCIPLE 4

THE ANATOMY OF A SEX STAR

Getting to Know Your Erogenous Zones

Your heart beats faster, the palms of your hands begin to sweat. Your tongue salivates. Your mind races, and your eyes become misty. Your stomach flutters, and your fingers tremble. You are entering—The Erogenous Zone.

The human anatomy is equipped with a bounty of erotic territories which have come to be known as erogenous zones—any portion of one's body that provides sexual arousal when stimulated. Unfortunately, most people know more about the inner workings of their automobiles than they do about their own bodies. How can anyone expect to have Terrific Sex if they don't know their perineum from their pudendum?

These days it is imperative that you know everything there is to know about your sex organs. Not only will you be more skilled at employing and exercising the various organs and muscle groups that augment your sexual enjoyment, but you will be better prepared in practicing the sensible sex guidelines because you will understand more fully how the body functions.

When was the last time you really examined your

genitals? If you're like most people, probably not since sixth or seventh grade when you spent hours in the bathroom, mirror in hand, staring in awe as puberty lay siege to your body.

Well, put this book down. Go get a mirror, and come right back. If you're reading on a bus or in some public place, I won't mind if you wait until you get home.

Okay. Take off all your clothes. Turn on the lights. Bring a lamp close to you, if necessary. You will want to have sufficient illumination that you won't be casting shadows over certain portions of your sexual anatomy.

Put the mirror where you can see yourself in all your glory. Remember God is in the details. Get the looking glass close enough so that you can see everything clearly.

It might interest you to know just how similar the male and the female sex organs actually are. Did you know that in the womb, a two- to three-month-old fetus, genitally speaking, is neither male nor female? It's hermaphroditic, sprouting what is called a genital tubercle. This little mound grows into the penis in the male and the clitoris in the female. Indeed, the clitoris and the penis share homologous sensitive tissues, although the average clitoris is considerably smaller than the average penis. The scrotum in the male and the labia majora in the female both evolve from what is imaginatively called the labio-scrotal swelling. Some men have a pronounced scrotal raphé, or demarcation running up the middle of their scrotum delineating where the scrotal lips merged. As you gaze into the mirror, guys, check to see if you have one, too.

I've always found it enlightening to know that what I'm sporting between my legs is not that fundamentally different from what the opposite sex is carrying around. This can help you to feel more comfortable when exploring your sex partner's genitals. After all, the opposite sex is not really so opposite.

Having absorbed this bit of sexual lore, let's jump right into our physical examinations.

A WOMAN'S WORLD

Ladies, let's direct our attention to your vulva—the external female sexual organs. Thanks to women's lib, a lot more women are growing comfortable with their genitalia. Betty Dodson, author of *Sex For One*, challenges women to become more "cunt positive," finding pride in the natural beauty of their sexual anatomy. The word "cunt" offends some, but in various times in history it was the preferred terminology. It stems from the Middle English word *cunte*, meaning woman. I happen to prefer the British slang "cunny," and I especially like the way my friend Dan describes the organ as "the glorious female pussy!" Perhaps the adjective "female" is redundant, but how true the sentiment! Your sex is gorgeous. Enjoy its aesthetic allure.

First let's look more closely at the LABIA MAJORA (or "greater lips"). These two large folds decorated with pubic hair respond brilliantly to manual stimulation while serving as protective walls for the female reproductive organs. The major folds meet at the MONS VENERIS on top and the PERINEUM on the bottom. The mons veneris (literally "mount of Venus," the love goddess) is a puff of skin situated over the pubic bone, which is covered by strands of thick pubic hair. The mons is remarkably responsive to touch and direct pressure, especially when such pressure pushes down on the sex organs below. The perineum is a band of muscular flesh that spans from the VAGINAL OPENING to the ANUS, and it feels great when it is rubbed or stroked. The anus, it should be noted, is also a potent source of considerable erotic charm.

Couched between the greater lips are the LABIA MINORA (or "lesser lips"). Don't let the name fool you. This is one example where less is truly more. These tender folds are extremely delicate—and are quickly moistened by lubricants secreted by accompanying sweat and sebaceous glands. Sometimes there is a spot called the FRENULUM where the labia minora unite on top. Nestled neatly beneath this area is the CLITORAL HOOD (or "prepuce") which serves as a cover for the GLANS of the CLITORIS.

The clitoris is the primary source of sexual stimulation in the female. Like its cousin, the penis, it is jam-packed with erectile tissue and excitable nerve endings. Unless you are a member of a certain African tribe, you shouldn't have any trouble finding yours. Those poor souls have to suffer through the idiotic practice of clitorectomy—in which the clitoris is cut off as an adolescent rite of passage. Ironically, there is another African tribe that devotes hours of each day to stretching the clitoris in hopes of enlarging it, since a large one is considered a status symbol.

The word "clitoris" is derived from the ancient Greek *kleitoris*, whose root means "key." Without a doubt, the clitoris is the key to a woman's sexual fulfillment. This fascinating organ comes in a variety of shapes and sizes. According to the *Encyclopedia Of Love And Sex* (Marshall Cavendish, Ltd., 1986), size varies from one-eighth of an inch to nearly a half inch in diameter. Women who have exceptionally large clitorises have been known to engage in a form of sapphic love-making called tribadism in which the clitoris is rubbed against, and sometimes penetrates, another woman's vagina.

An important muscle that lies just below the clitoris, and which separates to either side is the BULBO-SPONGIOSUS MUSCLE. At the moment of orgasm this little band contracts rhythmically, helping to induce wave after wave of sensual pleasure. It also facilitates the movement of the clitoris back underneath the clitoral hood, which occurs frequently at the apex of an orgasm.

While regarding your clitoris, it might help you to visualize the PACINIAN CORPUSCLES, minute fibers that make up the clitoral glans and certain sections of the immediate vicinity. These tiny nerve endings are supremely susceptible to touch and the slightest bit of pressure. Think of them as you lightly caress and manipulate the head of the clitoris.

Located just below the clitoris, you'll notice the URETHRA, which, as you undoubtedly know, is the tube from which urine is excreted. While it is sensitive to touch, you should avoid inserting anything directly into it, even your fingernail.

Now we're coming to the well of loveliness—the VAGINA—without a doubt the most important member of a woman's sexual apparatus since it doubles as the birth canal and the receiving area for the penis during coitus. The vagina is usually ten centimeters long and is angled upwards at sixty-five degrees. When not in use during sex or giving birth, the pink, moist VAGINAL WALLS lie close together. In females who have not experienced intercourse, nature has designed a HYMEN (sometimes known as the maidenhead) which just about closes the opening of the vagina. The use of tampons has caused many women to break their hymens prior to losing their virginity. This has no effect whatsoever on sexual arousal.

You may have heard about the celebrated G-SPOT and are wondering if you have one of your own. It is still a subject of great controversy, although the book *The G-Spot* by Alice Kahn Ladas, Beverly Whipple, and John D. Perry certainly makes a strong, convincing case for its existence and prominence. I recommend their book to you as an informative, engrossing study of female sexuality. What is a G-Spot and how do you find yours? Dr. Ernst Grafenberg, whose initial has become the name of the erogenic zone, believed the G-Spot is located "along the sub-urethral surface of the anterior vaginal wall." The authors of *The G-Spot* describe it as lying "directly behind the pubic bone within the front wall of the vagina. It is usually located about halfway between the back of the pubic bone and the front of the cervix, along the course of the urethra . . . and near the neck of the bladder, where it connects with the urethra." It is suggested that you learn to feel this all-important area by exploration with your finger. Once you locate and isolate it, you can awaken its spirit.

Let's not overlook the BREASTS, which although not technically part of the female genitalia, are certainly erogenous zones. Stimulation of the breasts has a direct link to sexual response in the vulva, setting off the cycle of sexual arousal and lubrication. Some women have been known to have orgasms simply by the stroking of their breasts. Despite their obvious role in nursing and motherhood, the breasts have evolved over the millenia into sexual organs which provide intense sexual gratification for both sexes. Looking more closely, we first notice the NIPPLE surrounded by a circle of darker skin called the AREOLA. It is now understood that women who have undergone pregnancy develop darker areolas.

You may be interested to know that Dr. Desmond Morris, author of *The Naked Ape*, suggests a woman's breasts, especially when they're large and full, have become sex symbols because they resemble buttocks. How's that for an inspired leap of the imagination! But Dr. Morris points out that humans are not the only mammals who find sexual gratification from fondling, kissing, and hugging breasts. He suggests that since human males do not regularly mount females from behind, the breasts have supplanted, or filled in, for the buttocks, which are a natural attraction to other primates.

A MAN'S WORLD

Gentlemen, here's your chance to peruse your private parts. I know you're proud of them, but aren't you fond of them too! How often we think of the penis as a separate entity with a mind of its own! But without the other sex organs it would be of little or no use. Together, they make quite a team.

Let's begin our odyssey at the SCROTUM, the thin-skinned sack, covered with wispy strands of pubic hair, which houses the TESTICLES. The scrotum is suspended midline from the pubic bone and hangs below and behind the penis. The organ is composed of two separate internal halves, divided by a membranous wall, or septum. Sequestered in the tissue beneath the skin of the scrotum are fibers of soft muscle called the DARTOS LAYER. These fibers pull up when exposed to low temperatures, and expand when in the presence of heat, which explains why your testicles move up tight against the pubic bone when you've been swimming in cold water, and droop down real low when it's very hot outside.

The TESTES produce male sex cells, SPER-MATOZOA, which as a group are better known as SPERM, as well as the male hormone, TESTOSTER-ONE. The average testicle measures about two inches in length and an inch across. The outer shell of the testicle is known as the TUNICA ALBUGINEA, a thick layer of white fibrous tissue. Generally, one testicle hangs lower than the other, as if arranged by nature to minimize the danger of the testes pressing together when sitting. These two oval bodies are very delicate and vulnerable. You can actually feel the veins and tubings of the gonads in your fingers. Remember they are not designed to be squeezed, otherwise you'll feel a wave of nausea and a great deal of pain. Realizing this, you may wish to be more careful in how you dress in the future. Squeezing your testicles into a tight pair of jeans may look great on the outside, but it can deleteriously affect the manufacture of SPERM which takes place within.

That clumpy section attached to the side of each testicle is called the EPIDIDYMIS. This sixteen foot coiled tube is where the sperm is stored at the onset of orgasm, and then ejaculated into the VAS DEFERENS. Located in the abdomen, the vas deferens, if unfolded, would stretch as much as twenty feet in length.

Also situated inside the body is the PROSTATE GLAND. According to *Forum* magazine, a journal of sex research, "without the prostate, sex would not be much fun at all. It is absolutely necessary to raise an erection and manage emission, ejaculation, and orgasm. Ninety-nine percent of the opalescent ejaculate originates in this key location, which is the very hub of men's internal sex organs." The prostate is a chestnut-like organ, "part gland/part muscle" that fits snugly around the URETHRA underneath the BLADDER. "Though referred to in the singular," *Forum* adds, "the prostate is actually a bundle of millions of microscopic glands interlaced with and surrounded by muscle and protected by a tough fibrous cap." If you are curious you can search for your prostate by inserting a clean, neatly trimmed finger a few inches inside your rectum. Pulling the finger back towards the genital region you will most likely feel the spongy doughnut-like shape. Don't apply too much pressure—and don't poke at it. Massage it gently. Stimulation of the prostate, as many men who have undergone rectal examinations know, very often induces an erection. We'll be talking more about this "Oh-Gee!" Spot later on.

Men will notice that they also have a PERINEUM, although theirs is thicker and more prominent than a woman's, feeling almost like an extension of the penis itself. On one end of this muscle sits the ANUS—on the other, the testicles, at the base of the penis.

The PENIS is most assuredly man's best-known sex organ. He can hardly go through life without being acutely aware of it. And it does have an uncanny ability to make its presence felt. But how much do you know about the structure of the penis? Inside the shaft lies the URETHRA, and at the tip we find a mushroom-shaped GLANS or CORONA. This is the most sensitive area of the PHALLUS and in its natural state it is covered by a FORESKIN. Circumcision is a practice that is still popular in the States, whereas most of the rest of the civilized world continues to leave well enough alone.

PRINCIPLE 5

SEXERCISE!

You're as Good
in Bed
as You Feel

In the days before I went to the gym, I had two deep-seated convictions. First, that people who had sensational physiques were born that way. Beauty was predetermined by genetics. Second, that only a lemming would fall for a trend like aerobics or use free weights to build up his body. Half the people I saw going in and out of health clubs didn't look very healthy. In fact, a lot of them looked pretty silly in those Reeboks and running sweats, with Heavy Hands and Walkmen. What I didn't understand is that fixing up your body, and attaining healthy good looks, is a process. Working out takes a great deal of effort. But the rewards, especially as they pertain to sex, are tremendous.

When I finally started to work out on a regular basis, my life was transformed. My chronic back pains disappeared. I stopped having tension headaches. I started to eat nutritious foods because I was hungry! I went from a 38 regular to a 40 long. My posture straightened out and I was suddenly taller! My bottom tightened, while my love handles diminished. I slept

49

well, falling asleep the minute my head hit the pillow. My concentration levels in my work increased. At one point I even burst into tears while bench-pressing because I suddenly realized I was a hunk!

Naturally, my sex life improved. People started to look at me differently. I had always been considered handsome, but now people were calling me "sexy." I dated people I had only dreamed about before. I discovered that my sexual stamina increased tenfold. I was hornier a lot of the time, because my hormones and glands were working at full tilt. I learned that a good cardiovascular system was the key to virility. It was fantastic! And all because I took the trouble of taking care of myself.

My story is not unlike that of many other people all across America who are making an extra-special effort at trimming down, dieting, eating right, sleeping adequately, avoiding stress, and exercising regularly. Haven't you noticed how many more attractive people there are around? We're finally accentuating how important it is to one's self-esteem and self-image that we strive to be good-looking and physically fit. This doesn't mean that you have to spend a fortune on cosmetic surgery, or run off to a fat farm to look like the Ford model next door. What it does mean is that you have to take responsibility for your appearance and your physical well-being.

As far as sex goes, you're as good in bed as you feel. If you're running out of breath, or constantly complaining about back problems, you're not going to be much of a turn-on. If you're out on a date, and you are tired from poor sleep, overworking, and lack of exercise, and you have dark circles under your eyes, no one is going to think you're sexy. People are generally attracted to human beings who are alert, awake and alive! They usually let sleeping dogs lie.

Now. Let's be truly honest about our bodies. Remember if you don't think you're attractive, no one else will either. Stand before the looking glass and make a thorough inventory of yourself. Are you out of shape (a nice euphemism for fat)? Could your arm be mistaken for your thighs? Do you find yourself trying to suppress a sigh every time you look in the mirror? Do you start weeping? Screaming? Then maybe it's time you did something about it.

I suggest you go to your neighborhood gym as soon as possible. Find one that is close enough to your house or workplace that you won't think up excuses why you can't go. Get a trainer and start working out regularly.

In terms of making love, there are a number of beneficial exercises that can be carried out everyday in your bedroom or living room. Not only can they be accomplished, they *must* be accomplished if you want to experience and excel at Terrific Sex. Do them in the nude, each morning or each evening, to some energetic music with a decent beat. You may wish to perform them with your lover, husband, or sex partner— or even a friend. The more the merrier.

HEAVY BREATHING

Before your lover takes your breath away, try this deep breathing exercise. Most people don't realize how important and helpful to one's health full, deep breathing is. First, it supplies oxygen to the entire body. Second, it facilitates in reducing tension. Third, it sets a pattern for successful breathing that can come in handy during strenuous activities like exercise, working out, sports, and that great American pastime—sex. You don't want to be left without sufficient air at the brink of orgasm. You want your blood to be healthy and to surge throughout your being from the skin on your scalp to the tips of your toes.

Likewise, you want to be ready to start hyper-ventilating during orgasm, since this is a natural stage in climaxing. Clearly, if your breathing is out of sync, your orgasm will suffer. On the other hand, if your breathing is good, you'll be able to increase your endurance and sexual prowess in the bedroom.

Right now I want you to focus your attention on your breathing. How deep do you go when you inhale? Are you taking shallow breaths? You should be inhaling enough air (through your nostrils) so that your lungs expand and stretch out at the bottom. The lungs are built into your diaphragm. Fill them up to the max. Already you can feel how satisfying a deep breath is.

Take another deep breath and hold it in for ten seconds. Slowly, let it out, tightening your lips—so that the air escapes in a thin gust. Continue until you have no air left. You are beginning to use all of your respiratory system. Hopefully, you will feel more relaxed and alert.

A final note. Take a balloon, or any inflatable item—whether it's an inflatable boat, air mattress, or even your favorite blow-up doll—and fill it up by breathing into it. Don't rush it. There's no reason to get blue in the face. We just want to exercise your breathing muscles, not strain them.

So, now you're better acquainted with your inhaling and exhaling routines. Practice them wherever you are, at your office desk, on the bus, in church. Later when you're in the throes of a much-needed orgasm, you'll be glad you did.

GETTING LIMBER

Flexibility is the second most important attribute of a dynamic lover. Although there are times when you will want to be stiff, for the most part, rigidity is not a bonus in the boudoir. You need to be limber so that you can move easily, quickly, and with grace whenever you switch positions, reach, stretch, and bend over. The last thing you want to do in bed is suffer a charley horse or throw out your back.

As the authors of *The G-Spot* recommend, "The muscles of the stomach, hips, and thighs are especially important to sexual experience and expression. If they are too tense, it may be difficult to move the pelvis independently of the legs and torso. If they are flaccid, it may be difficult for the pelvis to move at all."

Here are a few simple exercises that will help you be more flexible while making love. They'll also help you in everyday circumstances to feel more relaxed and less irritable, which in turn, might help you win the heart of someone you're really crazy about.

a) THE NECK RELEASE—Stand up straight, face forward. Now gently, drop your head to one side and, slowly but freely, roll your head down and then around to the other side. Do this three times on each side. If you experience intense resistance or pain, don't push yourself. The operative word here is elasticity. Go easy on yourself. You want to free the neck and shoulder muscles, not force them to respond.

b) THE SIDE STRETCH—Standing straight on both feet, lift both hands over your head. Now gradually move your entire upper torso to one side, trying not to move your legs, hips or stomach. Bring your arms straight out, but tilted a bit sideways. Do this three times on either side. At first you won't get very far, but eventually, in time, you'll be able to bend halfway over to one side.

c) THE SIDE SPIN—Put your hands straight out to either side, palms flat, fingers stretched out. Now spin right to left, left to right, back and forth, twenty-five times. Pretend you're the spinning device of a washing machine. This will release pockets of pent-up energy throughout your upper body and allow for greater flexibility.

d) THE LEG STRETCH—Last, but not least, sit on the floor, or on a mat, feet stretched out straight in front of you. Point your hands towards your feet, knees slightly bent, and then bend forward. You don't need to touch your toes, not yet at least. Nor should you bounce. If you feel your hamstrings tightening, breathe out, relax your legs, and pull back your arms. The secret here is to stretch the leg muscles, not cause them to contract. This exercise is dreaded by many because they perform it incorrectly. Don't push the body towards the feet, let it fall forward naturally.

GETTING TIGHT

As one lady friend put it, to enjoy great sex "you need a strong stomach, and a tight ass."

The lower abdomen should be strong and well-supported in order that the groin and genital area can be free from strain, extra weight, and flaccidness. Try this simple exercise:

THE FLAT TUMMY—Lay on your back, hands flat by your side. Now lift your feet six inches into the air. Feel how taut the muscles just above your genitals are! Hold your feet up for a count of three, then ease them down. Do this ten times. Please, if you feel that the exercise is pulling painfully on your lower back, proceed with caution. Try one leg at a time, if this is the case.

While this exercise will assist you in tightening the muscles just above your pubic bone, it won't help you lose that roll of flab or potbelly you're lugging around. That you'll have to lose by dieting.

THE BETTER BOTTOM—Kneeling down, on all fours, your back parallel to the floor, lift one leg and swing it back behind you, pointing your heel up and away. Raise it as high as it will go without straining. Breathe out as you lift the leg. Breathe in as you pull it back towards your chest. Switch legs. Perform this eight times, adding more as you become more comfortable with the routine in the days ahead.

Another good exercise for the buttocks is THE FANNY HILL. Stand before the staircase in your home. If you don't have one, find a small stepladder or even just a strong, sturdy wooden box or trunk. Step up, one or two steps, then step back down. Do this repeatedly twenty-five times. It will help strengthen your gluteal muscles, which you'll soon see are very important when it comes to flexing your "love muscles."

THE LOWER SPINE

Perhaps no other body area is as significant during the sex act as the lower spine—especially during orgasm. For instance, when a man climaxes, the lower spine takes over from the brain. His hips begin to thrust back and forth automatically. This movement will happen regardless of the position he is in, or the act being performed. Even during masturbation, it is an essential aspect of orgasm. Women, too, will find that a limber lower spine adds to their sexual enjoyment by allowing them to return thrusts, creating dramatic sexual friction.

Here are a few pointers to develop this area.

THE CRANE—Lying flat on the floor, face down, hands by your sides, push up your back with your arms, then lift your head towards the ceiling for a split second. Feel the tension in your lower back. Ease into the position.

Follow this up with THE PLOW. Still lying face down on the floor, lift your legs up about a foot off the floor. Spread them apart, then bring them back together and slowly ease them back down. Do this ten times.

Good. You're now ready to try some really sexy exercises!

THE SQUEEZE PLAY

According to ancient Greek mythology, the reason the Sphinx was so threatening to all the men who challenged her was that she seduced them into intercourse, trapped them between her powerful thighs, than grasped them with her astonishing vaginal muscles. Indeed, the word sphincter, which simply refers to any ring-like muscle that squeezes shut, is directly derived from this mythic creature.

The riddle, then, for us, is how do we master our vaginal and sphincter muscles to create our own brand of animal magnetism? The answer, luckily, is not as difficult to come by as the one Oedipus provided. All we have to do is learn to use our PUBOCOCCYGEUS (PC) MUSCLE.

The PC Muscle has nothing to do with your personal computer—and has everything to do with your sexual performance. This muscle group supports the genital region, the anus, and the adjacent internal organs. It plays an important role in achieving orgasm. "The better the health of the PC Muscle," say the authors of *The G-Spot*, "the more enjoyment women and men are likely to derive from sexual relations." Best of all, the Pubococcygeus Muscle can be trained. You may not be able to pronounce the word, but you can certainly put it into action.

The PC Muscle stretches from the pubic bone in the front to the coccyx (or tailbone) in the rear. It is this muscle that enables pets to wag their tails to show how happy they are. For humans, it helps bring a smile to many a grateful lover.

THE PRELUDE TO TERRIFIC SEX

Locating the PC Muscle is easy. Mentally think of the muscle you use when holding in a full bladder. Now contract that muscle. You will probably recall having used it before. When you push down on it, you will create a sensation that is reminiscent of a bowel movement. These are the two directions the PC Muscle can take. Ironically, we associate this muscle with "going to the bathroom" far more often than we do with "going all the way."

Now that you've isolated the muscle, in terms of feeling, I want you to watch it in action. If you are alone, get out that mirror again and look closely at your perineum while you pinch this muscle. You will probably see a slight movement take place. The more you isolate the muscle, the less you will depend on moving your stomach, hips and thighs. Pretty soon, you will see how the slightest indication from your mind can make you flex the muscle. Men have become skilled at isolating this muscle when flexing their erect penises.

If you are a woman, you may wish to insert a finger inside your vagina and feel the effect of the muscle pinching. Put in two fingers and spread them apart in a V-for-Vagina position, then press down on either side with your vaginal muscles and try to clamp your fingers together. Why not try contracting and releasing your PC group ten times in a row, for three full sets. Dr. Ruth has suggested that every time you come to a halt at a red traffic light or stop sign to contract and release your PC muscle.

Bravo! By now you're on the road to becoming a true dynamo in bed. Nothing is guaranteed to improve your sex life like a good, working knowledge of your sexual muscles. You're ready to tackle a more puzzling area—your very own Sex Bio.

PRINCIPLE 6

DISCOVERING YOUR SEX BIO

Let's face it. If you're hung up about sex, reading a how-to manual isn't going to improve your sex life. Before we can get into the specifics of having Terrific Sex, it's important to ask if we really want it. We have to look at our past and present lives and see what patterns have defined our sexuality over the years. Like any good mystery, it requires serious detective work.

This is the most difficult undertaking you will face on the road to Terrific Sex. Getting honest with yourself and doing the homework that is necessary to uncover and probe into your unpublished, unexpurgated, unabridged sex life.

One of the benefits of the AIDS crisis for me has been in discovering who I am sexually, and letting go of who I thought I was. For so many years I was completely wrapped up in making sure that other people got what they wanted. Sex was only as good as the reception it got. I lived perpetually in search of approval. Sex for me was something you did to another person. It had nothing to do with how I felt, or what I needed emotionally.

How did I come to change? First, I had to own up to my obstinance. My selfish "selflessness." The more I gave pleasure, the more I got. But I never let anyone give me pleasure. I preferred to take it.

The sexual crisis changed everything for me. I was no longer comfortable having sex with strangers. It was unsafe—and unrewarding. I soon discovered that I didn't know the first thing about cuddling, intimacy, petting, touching, kissing, and hugging. In short, I was pretty lousy at making love. I had to learn from scratch. At times I felt like an awkward teenager going through the motions for the first time. But it has been worth the effort, because for every little step I've taken, I've come closer to experiencing sex as a mutual experience—not a selfish one.

I came to this understanding only after an intense scrutiny of my past. I made a list of all those people I had been to bed with—and some where a bed hadn't proved necessary. In my case, the list was very long. What I discovered, merely by putting the names to paper, was how similar most of the people I slept with were. There was a definite pattern cropping up the more I explored, the more I wrote down, the more I remembered. I had continually gravitated toward people who would only expect to be pleased. I did not choose sex partners who would be there for me. This was a painful realization, because I was so sure that I had always been happy and fulfilled sexually. That was my attitude—and the image I projected. But the fact of the matter, based on what I could read in front of me, was quite the opposite. I might have been *sated* during those hundreds of encounters, but I don't think I can say I was truly satisfied.

Other surprising truths were revealed to me through this process, a few of which I now realize form the basis, the very foundation, of my sexual being. Only by exposing these tender, sometimes haunting memories, have I been able to accept them and to use them constructively in defining my sexuality today.

Researching your Sex Bio has obvious advantages in the age of AIDS. First of all you have a good idea whether or not you might have been infected. The vast majority of you reading this book luckily don't have to worry about that. For you the Sex Bio can point the way to increasing your sexual enjoyment while serving as preparation for outlining a sensible sex strategy. It can also develop your sexual wisdom by:

a) detailing which sexual acts you find the most appealing and those for which you have a natural proficiency.

b) demonstrating what type of man or woman you are consistently drawn to.

c) pointing out the origins of your sexual tendencies or proclivities.

d) indicating which fetishes have always intrigued you—and those you may wish to explore.

e) showing how mood-changers like alcohol and drugs have influenced when and with whom you end up having sex.

f) unraveling the secret sides of your erotic personality you've never dared reveal before.

g) exposing bad habits, such as improper hygiene, compulsiveness, and impulsiveness that disrupt your generally well-ordered routine.

h) revealing that you have too often simply succumbed to peer pressure rather than developed a confident, workable idea of what you desire and require.

Ultimately, your Sex Bio can shine some much-needed light on your strengths and weaknesses.

For instance, if you have a hard time expressing your sexual wishes, you're probably better off choosing a partner whom you have learned to trust before having sex.

If you realize that you've never questioned what type of sex life the men or women you've dated have had before you encountered them, now is the time to move beyond such naiveté. Learn how to ask.

If you figure out that you've dated more than one man or woman who is an intravenous drug user, you can begin to keep an eye out for telltale signs the next time you get involved with someone new.

Or if you discover that you prefer so-called foreplay to intercourse, now is the time to see this as an advantage, rather than as a character flaw. Use this information in viewing safer sex as a positive alternative. "Penny," a secretary, realized that she always preferred mutual masturbation to oral sex and intercourse. Now she looks forward to engaging in this activity rather than dreading the rejection of her partner.

"Veronica," the young woman we encountered earlier, found that she had to reevaluate her sex history when the reality of the AIDS threat hit her squarely in the face. She had been "very promiscuous" for a period of five years prior to settling down with her fiancé. She had to deal with her sexual record because she feared her sexual past might be a threat to her current relationship. Had she been exposed when she was out there? "It made me feel like I was morally paying for something," she says about her guilt. "My entire sexual past came out at me like the cast of characters in an ongoing soap opera. Everyone I'd ever been with came back to haunt me. Faces flashed through my mind. I hadn't remembered everyone and all the situations I'd been in. Sometimes memories would pop up at the most bizarre times, like once it happened in the middle of a business meeting. It seemed so unfair to suffer like that. But now that I'm on the other side of it, I can tell you that I learned a great deal about my attitudes about myself and my sexual nature."

For Veronica, the rewards far outweighed the pain. Her personal version of a Sex Bio dramatically altered her personality for the better. "The whole mechanism of what used to make me tick is gone," she says excitedly. "Now it's me. It's the first time I feel like the captain of my own ship. It's caused me to take a stand that I should have taken before. I still buy into that crap about a woman being passive, and a victim, and all that, but *I'm* here now. I can say to a man, 'Listen, these are my requirements.' I could never do that before. I used to say, 'Let's just cast this bubble in the wind and see where it goes.' Today, I have a clear picture of where I want to go."

If you are just beginning a relationship, or finally opening up in one, you'll want to research your experiences of the last decade. In particular, go back and review the last seven years. What was your sex life like? How many people were there? The answer can be anywhere from zero to hundreds, but how did it affect you? Are you monogamous in spirit, but not in fact? Before you discuss these issues with the person with whom you intend on having a sexual relationship, it might prove helpful to do more digging into your sexual past.

Besides the list of people you've been with, ask these and other relevant questions:

When did you first become aware of sex?

How old were you when you first kissed someone?

What did it feel like? Was it a positive or a negative experience? What was the setting?

When was the first time you saw someone of the opposite sex naked? Was it an actual experience, or did you look at a magazine or a movie?

How did you get along with dating and going

steady in high school? Do you think of these early memories as happy ones? Or was socializing in high school an ordeal?

Who was your first sexual experience with? Your friend, a date, a stranger?

Was it with your brother or sister? For some of you incest might be an issue. How has it affected the way you feel and think about sex today?

Was your first sexual experience with someone older? Younger? The same age? What took place? Did you make the first move? Did you feel comfortable doing it? Afraid? Was there someone else there besides the person you were having sex with?

Probe your memory bank. Search out all the relevant details. Don't be cursory. Take this suggestion very seriously. Your answers are extremely important to the way in which you perceive sex today. Often, those early experiences have the most influence on your later ones. In terms of your sexual fantasies they are of primary significance. What you did and how you were treated in those early sex encounters determine how you respond today. Those early experiences set patterns. Some good. Some not so good. Are you in a set pattern? Does it work for you—or are you unsatisfied, eager for a change. Do you dream of a different type of sex life entirely? Do you define yourself by rigid dualities, like Good or Bad? Prude or Sex Maniac? Whore or Madonna? Stud or Nerd?

Look into your closet and be honest about your sexuality. Have you ever had sex with members of your own sex? How did it happen? How did it make you feel? And now? Do your attitudes regarding homosexuality live up to your own experience? Do they affect your hetersexual relationships? Is there an inconsistency? If you are homosexual, look honestly at your past heterosexual experiences.

Don't be afraid. Your Sex Bio is your business, and your business only. If it is any comfort, Kinsey discovered that most Americans had experienced some type of homosexual experience. In fact, thirty percent of American males have had one or more sexual encounters with a member of their own sex. And that is sex occurring after adolescence that culminates in orgasm.

What about dual lives? Do you behave one way with the person you love and a different way with someone you're just having sex with? Do you "cheat" all the time? Are you uncomfortable with monogamous relationships? One-on-one affairs?

Write it all down in longhand. Type it out if that feels more comfortable. Write it in code, if you prefer. If you don't like writing, talk your story out loud into a tape recorder (or if you're brave and uninhibited share it with another person you can trust).

Keeping a physical, tangible record of your Sex Bio is advantageous because it's something concrete that you can hold on to, look at objectively, and refer to at a later date. If you want to maintain privacy, store your Sex Bio in your safe-deposit box, or get a locked diary.

You'll be surprised how much revealing, thought-provoking stuff will come out. First loves, lost loves, past loves, great loves, and some very sexy souvenirs. Some of them might even shock you. There will probably be some painful memories too. But that's part of the beauty of the process. Exhume these long-buried regrets and resentments. Only when you've spelled it all out will you be able to look at it as a whole. See it for what it really is at face value. Then you can define and *refine* your sex life along choices you've made and outlined for yourself. You'll be free to select a sex life that fits your personal needs and requirements.

PRINCIPLE 7

THE TERRIFIC
SEX PLAN

The moment you decided to practice safer sex, you started to live by a Sex Plan. You took the initiative of putting some order and sense into your sex life. It was a positive statement of self-affirmation, underscoring your willingness to place your health and happiness ahead of mere sexual gratification. Yet, even if the threat of AIDS were nonexistent, a Terrific Sex Plan would be an indispensable tool in increasing your sexual satisfaction.

Think of it the way you would a diet. You don't have to cut down on the amount you're having, but you can choose a regimen that promises better health, provides the daily requirements of love and affection, and adds considerably to your self-esteem.

Now more than ever, you have a right to be particular about your sex life. You should be able to choose when, where, how, and with whom you have intimate relations.

How many times have you treated sex as something wonderfully unexpected? Out of the ordinary? Yet waiting for sex to suddenly happen is a cop-out.

The Terrific Sex Plan

If you want Terrific Sex you're going to have to go out and get it. This is where a Sex Plan comes in.

Start by doing the second stage of your sex homework. Draw up a strategy, a routine, a schedule that outlines the type of sex that satisfies your needs and desires. Be reasonable. If you want it every night, make sure it's feasible. Be careful what you ask for; you might get it.

Pick a Sex Plan that you can manage. If you want to slow down, to set up boundaries between you and a demanding spouse, or an overzealous lover, then figure out a fair compromise.

If you keep succumbing to your sexual urges without any regard to your health or well-being, or if you feel that certain sexual experiences are worth taking risks for, a Terrific Sex Plan can help you resolve these troublesome behavior patterns.

Now is the best opportunity you'll ever have to adjust your lifestyle to accommodate the very real threat of AIDS. Be serious without being severe. Choose a Sex Plan you know you can count on.

As with the Sex Bio, you may wish to write down your Sex Plan in your diary or in a notebook. If you're more industrious, why not use a pocket calendar? Ultimately, the most valuable Sex Plan is the one you remember in your head. If you are really serious about organizing your sex life to fit your new lifestyle, then you should be willing to take whatever steps are necessary to achieve it.

One way in which a Sex Plan would work is while you're dating. Compile a Date Book. Figure out in advance how you are going to behave. The scheme should apply to anyone you're dating, whether she acts like Donna Reed, or Nancy the Nympho— whether he's Prince Charming, or Rodney Dangerfield. If you respect yourself first and above all else, then no one man or woman can shake you from your personal commitment.

AN OLDIE BUT A GOODIE

A typical Sex Plan is that old standard—"No sex on the first date." How old-fashioned can you get! But there it is. Pure and simple. Easy to comprehend and to manage. You promise yourself that you won't fool around—at all—the first time you go out. This relieves you of the bother of having to make up your mind during the date and wasting valuable time fretting needlessly over what might take place later on.

Why is such a personal commitment necessary? Because you can't trust someone you hardly know. But that is exactly what thousands of people do while dating when they take a new face home with them on the spur of the moment. One assumes a great deal of trust.

First, that this stranger is not going to cause you bodily harm.

Second, that this person genuinely is attracted to you, and that he or she is not going to have any misgivings about the encounter. Many times this type of assumption is patently off-base. Most people have a great deal of misgivings about casual sex. It is rare that two strangers can feel totally comfortable with each other without lapsing into a fantasy mode in which neither person is dealing objectively with the other. Oftentimes, it's because of this discomfort that a sexual tension is created.

Third, and for our purposes the most relevant, we

trust that the other person is not infectious with a number of sexually transmitted diseases. We tend to overlook the very real possibility that they may have gonorrhea or syphilis—or both! If we *didn't* overlook such things, there wouldn't be any cases of VD! The same holds true for herpes. When the television blares at you that 20 million Americans have some form of herpes, you have to wonder if the perfect stranger you've picked up might not be one of them. Still, for many of us, it is difficult to broach the subject. Here are some tips on how you can.

SAFE SEX NEGOTIATION

It's imperative you discuss your options for safer sex as early as possible before you reach the point of no return. This is the most difficult problem people are encountering in these fearful times. How do you talk about romance in the same breath as AIDS without taking away all the fun and mystery?

The best advice is—don't postpone the topic. The longer you delay in bringing AIDS up, the harder it will be to mention it—and the more you have to lose. One dating service has come up with the enterprising, yet ultimately foolish, notion that all singles interested in having sex should sport little safety pins on their lapels or elsewhere on their person in order to announce to their prospective lovers that they are into safer sex. Obviously, you can't resort to simplistic gimmicks when the moment arises. You're going to have to rely on your own good sense.

THE PRELUDE TO TERRIFIC SEX

Take for instance the following incident, recounted by "Michele," a twenty-nine-year-old banker from Washington. "I was down in New Orleans for Mardi Gras," she told me. "While having a few drinks at Pat O'Brien's I met a great-looking guy. Tall, green eyes, and curly brown hair. We arranged to meet for dinner after the parade, and when we finally got together I couldn't believe how I was feeling. It felt like love. I kept thinking—I'm a good judge of character. I can tell this guy is not a sleazebag. He really likes me. Later that night we went back to his place and made out for a long time. Then, he said he wanted to make love. I told him that I was scared of sleeping around with people I didn't know that well. He told me I was just being ridiculous and reading too many magazines. We ended up fucking without a condom. He didn't have one, nor did I. The whole time we were together, I couldn't stop thinking that maybe I was going to die. The thought of not knowing for five years made me sick to my stomach. Overall, it was a lousy experience. I wish it had never happened."

The story of Michele's trip to New Orleans is an example of a very common problem. Michele could have avoided all her anxiety if she had simply refrained from going home with a person she didn't know. She didn't have a workable Sex Plan. What she needed more than anything was not a condom. What she needed was *conviction*.

When you meet someone with whom you really hit it off, keep in mind that sex appeal is not only an energy that someone exudes, but a projection of your own sexual fantasies. All the ingredients are there for a fantastic night of love and romance. Except one very important one. *Reality*. The problem is you don't know anything about this person other than what you see before you. So this person you've fallen for on the first date appears to be someone very, very special. All the more reason to start laying down the laws.

Here, the Terrific Sex Ground Rules can provide a sound course for choosing realistic and appropriate approaches to safe sex negotiation. Let's review those that apply.

1) It's Not Who You Are, but What You Do. If you are going to have sex on the first date, keep in mind that it's your behavior that's going to get you into trouble, not the person you're with. Don't do what Michele did and judge a book by its cover. Hoping that someone is not infectious is not a logical means of prevention. Likewise, don't waste time depicting yourself as a clean-cut, previously pure, well-balanced, but straight-laced type. Just be yourself. You can change your behavior without reshaping your personality.

Use the tools available to you to send the right message to the person you're dating. Clarify your requirements. Start talking openly about all you've been reading regarding AIDS. If you dazzle your date with your expertise, he is going to be extra-sure he practices safer sex. He is not about to step on *your* toes.

How do you start up a safer sex conversation? One good approach is to say to your date, "you seem like someone who cares about his health . . ." and then ask him if he has read or heard about safer sex. This is a good way of bringing up the subject without putting your date on the spot by interrogating him. Let him take the ball and run with it. If you aren't satisfied with his responses, give examples of your own adjustments.

Also, prior to winding up in the bedroom, discuss the emotional side effects of the current AIDS crisis. Don't pretend it doesn't bother you. Tell him how you feel about the threat. You don't have to lapse into a monologue, reciting your Sex Bio, but share with him how you've become concerned and have altered your lifestyle appropriately.

Sure, it's awkward talking about the intricacies of safer sex. Hopefully, as more of us take the initiative, it will be increasingly less so. But for now allow yourself to feel uncomfortable. Admit it right up front. Your date might also be feeling awkward—and you both can laugh about it, and feel closer because of it. In circumstances like these, admitting fear is a courageous act.

2) ABC—Always Be Careful! Even before you begin safe-sex negotiations, take the steps you need to be adequately prepared. Clearly, it saves you a lot of hassle if you already have a condom with you (either at home, in the car, in a bag, or pocket, etc. . . . .). Suggesting safer sex techniques then won't entail the added difficulties of having to purchase a prophylactic at inappropriate times, such as in the middle of a date or, worse, after you've already undressed and are both lying under the covers!

The ground rule ABC can also be applied to the way in which you enact a Sex Plan. Don't jump into situations where sex becomes an issue unless you are psychologically prepared for it. If your Sex Plan does not include sleeping together while dating, don't accept an invitation to spend the weekend alone with this person. You're better safe than sorry.

3) When in Doubt, Check It Out. This rule works just as well in feeling each other out as it does during sex. If you've met someone and they assure you that they only "practice safe sex," don't be afraid to ask, "What is your definition of safer sex?" In my time, I've heard too many bizarre variations that have little to do with avoiding the exchange of bodily fluids. If your friend thinks oral sex without rubbers is safe, but you don't, spell it out to him. Stick by your plan. There's no need to get into an argument. If it helps you to feel more convincing, keep a few safer sex pamphlets around that you can refer to when necessary. Lend him this book! He'll be grateful you've demonstrated your concern. You'll be doing both of you a favor, while spreading the word.

4) K.I.S.S.—Keep It Sexy, but Simple. This slogan is the key to making the most of your safer sex negotiations. Talk about safer sex in erotic ways. Tell your date you're attracted to him. There's no harm in complimenting someone—and you're letting that wild passionate desire release some of its built-up energy. Try not to send mixed messages, as in saying, "I'm hot for your bod, but I'm just too tired to do anything about it." Don't make up excuses. The AIDS threat is a perfectly legitimate one. The issue is safe sex, not whether you're in the mood. Don't twist him in every direction either. Just tell him the truth. If the guy likes you, he won't even argue. He'll agree with you. If he only wants to have sex right off the bat, you're probably better off without him.

Similarly, there's no need to complicate the issue by adding comments like, "I wish we could do this, but . . ." Think how much nicer it is to stand firmly behind your desire to have good, clean sex. Try saying, "I *want* to make love to you safely, without fear, because I trust and respect you and I want you to trust and respect me." In this spirit, sex becomes a terrific means of communication, of building a bond between two loving people, of establishing and maintaining trust and intimacy.

Above all, don't feel compelled to go into a lengthy, baroque explanation regarding your Sex Plan. At such times, "No!" is a complete sentence. You have a right to your privacy in such matters. If you don't like him, by all means, don't beat around the bush. Be polite, even considerate, but don't be a people pleaser. If he complains that you're just being silly, call him on it. Don't allow yourself to be maligned or abused. Move on to bigger and better things.

Dress Rehearsals

Another excellent tool for safer sex negotiations is advance rehearsal. How do you get to be good at talking about safer sex? Practice. Next time you're with a close friend, explain how you need some help in working out a sensible safer sex scenario. Tell her or him that you'd like to experiment with a dress rehearsal, a role-playing game where you act out what might happen in the bedroom with your boyfriend or girlfriend. Your pal will probably be enthusiastic to participate because he or she is undoubtedly going through the same thing.

Try out different opening statements and various approaches until you find the one that you feel most comfortable with. Talking about safer sex is really no different than talking about other intimate details of courtship. At first you might be stammering like you did the first time you ever asked someone out on a date. But with practice, the words will soon come more easily. And when the moment arrives when you're really going to need them, you'll be ready. You'll know all the right things to say.

In Sex We Trust

The longer you've known someone, the easier it is to open up and let it all hang out. "Brian," an advertising director, told me of his latest romance. "I've been going out with Sheila for two months at least and I think we both know something special is happening between us. In the past we've talked about AIDS and our sexual histories, but not really in the context of us having sex. One night, a little while ago, we'd had a fabulous time and we were both feeling very romantic. We again talked about safe sex. And I told her I wanted to try it with her. Sheila said she was afraid to do it because she thought it might ruin our relationship. Her attitude was that safe sex was clumsy and too clinical. She was worried it would destroy any spontaneity between us. Once she said that, I knew it was going to be fine because she wasn't afraid of expressing her feelings, of letting me see her fears. I told her that if the sex didn't work, we could stop at any point one of us felt uncomfortable, and that in the end, the sex wasn't so important to me. What really mattered was that we continue seeing each other. I think putting it to her like that really helped her to see that I was here for more reasons than sex. I really care about her.

"At home we went through the whole routine of putting on the rubber together and we had a ball. We talked about our feelings at each stage of our lovemaking. It was wonderful! Because we both could see how much we trusted the other. And I respected her more than ever because she allowed me in, to see her vulnerable side. If anything, having safer sex strengthened our relationship."

Sometimes it takes more time. I know of one couple who promised to postpone sex for ninety days, all the while conducting a period of intense, romantic courtship with flowers, candles, limousines, theater tickets, and marvelous dinners in secluded restaurants. They found that setting boundaries beforehand opened the door to greater intimacy and mutual understanding. After ninety days, they both were sure they wanted to have sex as an expression of their affection for each other, not merely as a means of satisfying their sexual curiosity.

Janet Geringer Woititz, the best-selling author of *Struggle For Intimacy*, writes that "a healthy relationship is not confined to a sexual relationship which must end in orgasm, but celebrates the sharing and exploring." The distinguishing characteristic of intimacy is a "love relationship with another person where you offer, and are offered, validation, understanding, and a sense of being valued intellectually, emotionally, and physically. The more you are willing to share, and be shared with, the greater the degree of intimacy."

Afternoon Delight

Other Sex Plans can be less constricting, but more specific. "Catherine" is an intern at a large hospital in Connecticut. She found that she was less responsible when she had sex late at night. She was too tired to practice the safer sex guidelines. She didn't have the energy to argue with a date about whether or not he should wear a condom. She was becoming more and more anxious. Then she hit upon a solution. Rather than giving up sex altogether, she decided only to have sex on weekend afternoons. This way she is always on top of the situation. She claims that planning it this way has created a pattern that she can enjoy and count on. Now she looks forward to her weekly adventures. The lazy afternoon gives her ample time to explore the myriad of delightful safe sexual practices to which she has become accustomed.

Obviously a Terrific Sex Plan doesn't have to be written in granite. It's always in your hands to decide what's right for you, and sometimes those needs change or evolve because of time, place, or circumstances.

THE REVIVAL OF THE CHASTITY BELT

The Chastity Belt, a garment that prevented women from indulging in intercourse, came into vogue in the Middle Ages because men wanted to guarantee that their wives didn't fool around. The belt was also popular because it acted as a VD prevention device. So long as a woman wore one, her husband could rest assured he wasn't going to get the dread "French Disease" (or "English Disease" depending on which side of the Channel you were living). Needless to say, such good fortune also depended on his own virtuous behavior.

These days sexual abstinence is undergoing a considerable revival. For many of us, the Chastity Belt has evolved metaphorically into an internal device, a mental mechanism we employ to simplify things. Can it work as part of a Sex Plan?

If we promise we'll be abstinent for a certain amount of time (for example, until a cure for AIDS is discovered) theoretically we won't have to worry about catching the disease. We'll be virtually free from the risk of contracting AIDS. At least that's how "Billy," a consultant to a large industrial concern, figured it. Billy's been chaste since he first heard of AIDS. He's now contemplating leaving his job and becoming a Catholic priest. The fact that he's "constantly horny, doesn't matter," he argues. "As long as I don't fool around, it's a moot point." The question, however, is how long can he stay away from sex?

True sexual abstinence is difficult to maintain. And in terms of AIDS, it has not proven itself to be a foolproof method of prevention.

First of all, it is well documented that repeated and long-term efforts at suppressing one's sex urges can cause stress—and stress has proven to be a serious immuno-suppressant. In fact, it is considered a cofactor in the development of AIDS.

Second, when we push down our sex drives, they sometimes bounce back with unexpected force, causing us to act out in ways that are harmful. Take for example, the story of "Roger." A forty-year-old magazine editor, he "gave up" on sex, ignoring the reality that sexual desire had always been a powerful, motivating force in his life. After just three weeks, he found himself in a bar, drinking too much to reduce his pent-up stress. He ended up going home with a woman he just met, saying "fuck it" when the issue of safe sex came up. He didn't bother to wear a rubber.

It is crucial to remember what type of sexual person you are before you suddenly opt for strict abstinence. Very often it is the person who has problems *accepting* his sexual desires who ends up abusing them.

Remember it is not sex that is dangerous, but the type of sex one is having. Moderation is the goal.

There are times, however, when abstinence can make the heart grow fonder—as in those instances when a person chooses not to have sex in order to postpone joy. In a dating situation it is very often a good idea to delay the pleasure of sex (with the understanding that it will eventually take place) because it alleviates the pressure of having to perform sexually with a person you do not trust. Eventually, as trust and affection develop, an even greater sexual desire is achieved. Shere Hite put it rather well in *The Hite Report* when she stated that the whole point of sexual arousal is to "prolong the pleasure and the feeling of desire, to build it higher and higher."

PROMISES AND PROMISCUITY

What about the other side of the coin? Is there a point where having too much sex can be bad for you? As already stated, if you so desire, you can have as much sex as you like, as often as you like, and with as many people as you like *as long as it's safe.*

What's safe for you might not be safe for someone else. If you don't have a problem with laying down the law and setting boundaries to your sexual experiences, you may be able to indulge your taste for multiple sexual experiences with a variety of people. In such situations, practicing sensible sex is the perfect way to show you care about another person. It demonstrates your respect for him even if your interests don't go beyond just enjoying sex.

Take "Kenneth," an extremely handsome "triple threat," a straight actor/singer/dancer. It has been hard for him to adjust to the new sensibility. "I have to say I've really cut back on my activities in the past five months. I got really paranoid," he says. "The rate of AIDS cases in women is rising faster than in men. It's not that I think about it day to day, but when I read about it in the newspaper, it brings it up again. The long and short of it is—I've cut back on sex. And I don't like it. I don't like it at all."

Kenneth has found it hard to adjust to the dating game after years of seducing women right off the bat. "I don't like dating. I like indiscriminate sex. Preferably anonymous. I like lots of sex with different people. I think it's boring to go out with one woman. I always have. It's the variety of women that turns me on." As a result, he has devised a Sex Plan that enables him to have indiscriminate, casual sex—but strictly on a safe sex basis. "I've decided only to have sex with women I've met through other people. Sometimes I wind up with a loser. But most of the people I've met have been really nice. I carry a rubber with me at all times and I make sure I always come outside a woman's body. Maybe my chances of catching something are not entirely out of the question, but at least I know I'm taking the proper precautions."

Ken's noticed a few changes in the type of women he's been encountering. "Women, I think, are getting more forward in what they want in bed. I think that is a good sign. They aren't as embarrassed to express what they want. They're more aggressive. I don't know if it's because I've grown older and am now encountering older women or whether the Sexual Revolution is finally filtering down." One thing hasn't changed, however—a woman's desire for something more permanent. "Women always want something more long term. And always have. Since time immemorial. AIDS isn't going to change that."

When you choose to be promiscuous, you run the

risk of choosing a Sex Plan that is beyond your own capacity. There is always the chance that increasing the number of your sex partners will put a strain on your ability to make careful judgments and to know when you are overstepping your own boundaries. It is certainly more complicated to try and set up a Sex Plan where you are juggling two or three or four simultaneous affairs. Remember the slogan that helps you put things in perspective. K.I.S.S. —Keep It Sexy, but Simple!

Compulsive Sex

Compulsive sex is a condition where one's sex drive is out of control. The consequences can be very severe. Patrick Carnes has written an excellent book on the subject called *Out Of The Shadows: Understanding Sexual Addiction* (Compcare Publications, 1986). "While our society," he writes, "is shifting to a more open attitude toward sexual expression, we still view the amount and kind of activity as a matter of personal choice. For the addict, however, there is no choice. The addiction is in charge."

If you think you might be a sexual compulsive, and you're continuing to engage in unsafe sex even though you've tried to set up a Sex Plan, then you'd better seek help.

A checklist of compulsive traits would include these questions:

Do you find yourself lying about the sexual side of your relationship with someone else?

Have you caught yourself picking up strangers in singles bars as you did in the old days, even though you know it might be dangerous?

Do you find yourself slipping more and more into

81

alienated and isolated sex, going to bed with someone even though you don't really want to?

Do you find yourself losing your ability to say no to people who want to have sex with you because you're drunk or stoned? Alcoholism and drug addiction have always been terrible problems, but now because they reduce inhibitions, they are a leading factor in the spread of AIDS.

If you happen to be sexually compulsive and married or involved in a monogamous relationship, and you engage in unsafe sex, even only once, you've broken a promise, and you've threatened your health and your partner's health by adding an unknown third person's sexual history into the relationship.

"Pamela" admits that even though she was in a monogamous relationship, she had a multitude of affairs. She couldn't help herself. "I was always a big flirt. Before AIDS, I used to screw around with a lot of people. Sometimes it was just for fun with a friend. Or just something to do to pass the time. I always told my boyfriend about them because he never saw any romantic threat in my having a brief encounter. But lately, I've been afraid to tell him. I don't want him to worry that I'm bringing something in the house. I've been really good lately, but sometimes I think I'm overreacting and that just this once it will be okay."

Denial once again is the culprit. Patrick Carnes believes rationalizations, lies, and beliefs are planted deep within the sexual addict. "The husband," he writes, ". . . who visits a prostitute and on his way home feels warmly towards his wife and family, tells himself that his time (with the prostitute) really helps him to be more sensitive and loving to his family."

You may not recognize any of your own sexual traits in these descriptions. But if you do, you can seek advice and counsel from your local chapter of Sex-aholics Anonymous, Sexual Compulsives Anonymous, and/or a sex therapist. If you recognize any of these characteristics in the person you're seeing, all the more reason to practice safer sex at all times. Better yet, you can now recognize these traits in people you will en-counter in the future. Being well informed about the nature of this disorder can assist you in making the appropriate decisions at the correct time.

COURT AND SPARKS: ROMANTIC SEX PLANS

"Marla" is an attractive thirty-year-old actress with a deep husky voice. During the last few years, she's dis-covered that her attitudes about sex and romance have evolved dramatically. "What we're experiencing now," she shared with me, "is a backlash from the seventies. We went out there and found out how painful it can be to treat your body as a machine. There was too much objectification. Who needs it? I'm harassed every day by guys on the street. But now, in terms of dating and romance, it's a whole new game with a new set of rules. Today people call me and ask me if they can set me up with someone. The old blind date routine. It's kind of neat. Everyone is feeling a little fragile emo-tionally. We're being more careful of our rights. To me, the AIDS scare has created a convergence of two is-sues. Liberation and freedom. Liberation from past prejudices and hypocrisy. Freedom to just be ourselves, even if that means we're going to be vulnerable and needy at times."

Almost everyone I interviewed for this book agreed that romance lies not in fantasy, as in the time-worn image of a white knight on a white horse rescuing a damsel in distress, but rather in *reality*. As one lady quipped, "That nonsense might work in the movies, but it doesn't play in real life." The secret of romance in the eighties is finding someone who is willing to listen, to be there for you, to share their life with you.

Romance is caring. It's affection and intimacy. But most of all it's *love*. The current reemphasis on dating and monogamy has opened the door for many people to discover the meaning of true love for the first time in their lives.

"David" is a self-proclaimed Colorado "ski bum" who hopes one day to be a writer. He had been very promiscuous during the seventies, slowed down in the early eighties, and now is involved in what he calls a "person-to-person" relationship. "As a product of the sexual revolution," he says, "I was more than eager to have sex all the time, and I succeeded pretty well. But when AIDS swept into town, I didn't know what to do. I'd never been on a date, or been out alone with a girl who might be girlfriend material. All my sex just sort of happened among friends, or the occasional stranger. So I reluctantly started to ask girls out on dates. You know, the movies, dinner, and maybe a show. I had to learn how to behave. I couldn't come on too strong because I wanted to see them again. I decided I would try dating each girl for three dates without even mentioning sex. After that if I didn't like her, I'd move on. In the old days, all I had to do was find someone else if I didn't get what I wanted. Now things have more value, and the selection is less. *People* have more value. Plus, it is important for me that women perceive me as a reliable, dependable, likable sort of guy."

The rewards of romance, David says, have been deeply enriching. "What I discovered, and what totally blew my mind, was that I actually enjoyed dating, and skipping the sex right up front. I started really talking to girls, telling them things about myself I didn't even know. I felt like I was learning a whole lot about life, too. A few months ago, I actually met someone at a party and it was that old line, 'love at first sight.' We went out on three dates, and by the end of that trial period I knew I was hooked. The feeling wasn't entirely sexual either. I mean, she was beautiful, but not just in terms of her body."

What is really refreshing about David's story is the way he handled the usually problematic issue of sex. "I used to be the kind of guy who if you said no to sex, I would blow you off. But when I met my girlfriend, I wasn't about to give her up just because we had to wait. I didn't want to hurt her by using sex as a priority. When we did start to make out, it was incredible. There was so much more going on during that kiss, things that were emotional, psychological, and metaphysical! Man, it was wild! Eventually, we both were sure we wanted to be together in a physically intimate way, and we did it. I found the sex to be a million times more exciting than if I'd just balled her the first time around."

Perhaps the best expression of the new focus on romance comes from our friend "Stacy," the cabaret singer. She told me that after years of fighting the stereotypes of serious commitment, she's having second thoughts. "I would love a partner who will come and live with me and fight with me, and work with me, and help me set up a home," she says. "I am so tired of living like a college student in a dorm condition. And I'm not talking about owning a Cadillac and a mink coat. I just want a set of four kitchen utensils that don't disappear all the time. I don't want to smell mildew in the bathroom anymore."

PART TWO

STATE-OF-THE-ART SEX

PRINCIPLE 8

THE SENSUAL ARTS

A KISS IS STILL A KISS

Do you remember those wonderful old expressions, *spoon, necking, making out, first-base*?

Of all the areas of sexuality that I touched upon when interviewing people, kissing was the one that inspired the most concern. Everyone wanted to know if kissing was safe. One woman told me, "If you can't kiss and feel comfortable kissing, you might as well commit suicide." Fortunately such extreme behavior is completely unnecessary. Kissing is not considered a risk factor in the transmission of AIDS.

Kissing has always carried risk—mononucleosis, pneumonia, tuberculosis, hepatitis, the occasional venereal disease, not to mention the common cold. But in terms of AIDS, the strictest view regarding kissing is that (and I quote from *The New York Times*): "minute amounts of AIDS virus have been found in the saliva of some virus carriers, but no cases of transmission by kissing have been documented. Experts say there is no danger in a peck on the cheek of an infected person but they recommend against any exchange of saliva and deep kissing with an infected person."

Not quite so solemn, the directors of the Gay Men's Health Crisis advocate a less cautionary stance on kissing, which is saying a great deal since they are the founding fathers of safer sex. "The virus has been found in saliva. It's rare and it's only a very small amount. So kissing is not considered dangerous."

Therefore, considering these minor proscriptions, I leave the decision to you. If you do kiss, make sure you rinse with mouthwash, before and after kissing. This might seem inconvenient if one is not at home at the time the urge to kiss hits. But it really is a simple matter of playing it safe and sensible. There are sample-size bottles of Listerine and Scope that can be purchased and carried in one's pocket, or in one's purse.

One thing to keep in mind are the risks taken in brushing one's teeth. A toothbrush or WaterPik or even flossing can create tiny tears and cuts in the gums. It is recommended by doctors that you don't brush, floss, or WaterPik before kissing since the cuts in your mouth make it far easier to spread germs and any viruses.

However, don't follow the example of one gentleman who said to me, "Well, in that case I'm never going to brush my teeth again!" Lack of proper dental care can inflame and infect the gums, causing bleeding gingivitis or periodontitis—conditions that are far worse in terms of infection risk than the normal wear and tear of proper brushing.

Despite these preliminary safeguards, kissing can

still be a thoroughly arousing experience. Indeed, kissing is the cornerstone of Terrific Sex. It is no accident that the French word *baiser* which means "to kiss" is also slang for having sex. It *is* a sexual experience.

Perhaps now more than ever we need guidelines to reacquaint ourselves with that old black magic since for the last two decades the art of necking has been completely upstaged by oral sex and intercourse.

Let's listen to what "Janet," a high-school math teacher, has to say about the joys of kissing. She considers herself a connoisseur. "For me," she says, "kissing is an art form. It's a serious talent and the best clue you can get as to what kind of lover a guy is going to be. It's kind of a litmus test. When that little thing in my stomach starts to flutter, I know this is the one. This is the guy who's going to get me going. But if the kiss is lousy, and he doesn't know what he's doing, you can pretty much be sure he's going to suck in bed. I once met this guy who looked like a model from a Winston ad—he was divine. But he didn't know the first thing about kissing. I was so bummed out. I stopped what we were doing, and walked out. I think he was pissed off, but, hey, I'm not going to waste my time."

Janet, however, had a good instructor. "I was taught to kiss by a gorgeous man from the Virgin Islands. He was a dancer and I was down on vacation with my family. I was only eighteen. He was your typical Caribbean Casanova. He was after every woman on the island. I kind of went out with him just out of defiance. But when we kissed he said to me, 'Not bad., Not bad? No one had told me I wasn't bad, which doesn't sound too good. He told me not to be so rough. To take my time and linger on his lips. No one had ever taught me before. If I hadn't been a virgin, I would have slept with him, and I would probably never have slept with another man again. That's how good he was. It was scary—how excited he made me feel considering all our clothes were on."

Janet's escapade underscores the essential truth that kissing can be just as sexually stimulating as other forms of sex. It should be handled with the same amount of tenderness, care, and dedication.

In my travels I've come across a variety of kissers. Some of them set off rockets and fireworks. But it's hard to describe what makes someone a talented embracer. As with all things ethereal, it's best to describe what makes someone a good kisser by cataloguing what doesn't.

Here is my list of "face-suckers" to avoid:

The Blowfish

You've probably encountered the Blowfish yourself. This kind of kisser keeps their mouth open just enough to create a tiny hole. Sometimes they suck in their cheeks, which only detracts further from any erotic appeal.

The Grand Canyon

This is the worst kind of kisser. They open their jaws so wide that you can see their uvula. It never occurs to them to relax. They press their gigantic opening against your mouth and usually lean their body tightly up against you. They want to devour you. These unfortunates have obviously never been given any honest feedback.

The Tongue Twister

If this type didn't concentrate so much on batting their tongue around inside your mouth, they might stand a chance of really hitting home. Yet, they concentrate all their energy on swirling, twisting, spinning, and turning their hyperactive tongue inside and outside your mouth. It's as if they're involved in a tongue-wrestling match. With this type of linguist, you're guaranteed to lose.

The Tongue Snatcher

Beware! When I was in college I once dated a Wagnerian opera singer who was a demon in bed. The only problem was that she had this horrible penchant for grabbing onto my tongue with her lips while we were kissing. As she pressed down on it, thereby keeping it from moving, she would tug at it until I felt that at any moment she would tear the muscle out of my throat. If you encounter the same, take my word for it—get away while you still can.

The Lip Smacker

This poor kisser is more content with simply smacking his or her lips against yours so that you never get any sensual contact. All you get is this horrible popping sound. No tongue action. No glistening moist lips. This person is probably afraid of intimacy.

93

The Face Licker

Not only is this number a health risk, since they're depositing their saliva up and down your cheekbones, around your nose and all over your forehead, making sure they engulf your chin, but they spend so little time actually kissing that you might come to think they're forever sixteen and never been kissed. If you happen to be dating such a person, keep in mind to bring a handkerchief with you, or wear a ski mask.

The Ear Drill

A probing tongue flicking within the confines of the ear can be very titillating. But the Ear Drill spends all his or her time digging deeper and deeper into your ear. Such intimate doings can be a real bonus during sex since the motion is so penetrating and evocative of the sex act itself, but this type of kisser has trouble relaxing and responding to casual foreplay.

The Deep Throat

French kissing has always been a bit more risqué than plain old American kissing in which the tongue remains inside the tongue-owner's mouth. But the Deep Throat can not restrain himself from thrusting his muscular member down into the furthest reaches of his beloved's esophagus. Gagging might ensue, not to mention severe forms of germ warfare.

The Vampire

With this cad, "necking" takes on an entirely new con-notation. This sucker devotes all his attention to the soft, sensitive area under the chin, below the ears, and the cherished terrain around the voice box. If he is a true leech he'll leave hickeys everywhere as testaments of his undying (or is that "undead") devotion, and vis-ible scars of your previous night's passion.

The Teeth Clinker

If you haven't run into this toothy nightmare, you're lucky. For some reason, I don't know if it's because he or she's got buck teeth or needs braces, they have a tendency to bang their teeth against yours.

The Bug Eye

Looking into someone's eyes while you're kissing can make for a soulful encounter, especially if the moment is full of passion and wonder. But the Bug Eye can not shut his eyes at all. He stares with great big startled eyes directly into yours, thus causing you embarrass-ment, dizziness, and fatigue.

The Purser

A close relative of the Blowfish, the Purser tends to pucker at the mere mention of the word *kiss*. He is con-stitutionally incapable of relaxing or being himself. He is a poseur.

Tobacco Rude

The taste of tobacco for some people is a sexual stimulus. But if the person you're kissing smokes more
than a few cigarettes (or heaven forbid, cigars) a day,
then his kissing is apt to be deleteriously affected.
Mouthwash or a breathmint can save the day in such
an emergency.

The Nose Job

I've been visited a number of times by nose lovers who
descend on my nasal appendage like virulent succubi
insistent on drawing the last breath of air out of me. I
suppose the nose sucker thinks he or she is being seductive, clever, and oh-so-terribly erotic. But the truth
is, they're interrupting a perfectly good kiss and
wreaking havoc with your nervous system.

The Hair Puller

Another beware! The Hair Puller starts out slowly,
gracefully running her fingers through your hair as she
kisses you passionately. Pretty soon, however, she's
tugging at the strands just a bit more than you'd like.
By the time she's got both hands on your head, and
her body is writhing like an animal in your arms, she's
ripping the hair from the roots, causing you to scream
in pain.

A variant of this disorder is the man who wraps
his fist around a woman's ponytail and tugs her head
back at breakneck speed as he plants a wet one on her
kisser. Thanks to Karl Lagerfeld, men now have to
worry about this problem, too.

What about those extra touches that help make kissing even better? Here are a number of pointers that are guaranteed to advance you to the head of the class. You can probably add a few of your own.

The Kiss-and-Teller

Scheherezade was a true Kiss-and-Teller. This variety of kisser devotes a lot of his or her time whispering sweet nothings in your ear, murmuring softly as he pecks your cheek, dives down onto your lips, and chats endlessly as he presses his body tighter and tighter against you until you blurt out a seductive response yourself.

The Humdinger

In this case the lover presses his lips against your skin and hums as he kisses you. He can buzz along the contours of your face, against your forehead, or along your eyebrows. Inevitably he will descend to the nether regions of your neck and drum up some excitement there.

Whiplash

Most people don't even consider using their eye lashes as a marital aid. But gently flicking your eyelashes against another's, or letting them flutter like giddy gypsy moths along the skin, can send thrills and titters of electricity jolting throughout your being.

97

The Handsome Kiss

As Anita Loos wrote in *Gentlemen Prefer Blondes*. "Kissing your hand may make you feel very good." But don't forget that it can also be very erotic. Lightly kissing your lover's fingers, the palm, the back of the hand and the wrist can lend a great deal of romance and sophistication to any kissing occasion.

The Body Kiss

Take it a step further and branch out all over your partner's beautiful body. Kiss his or her arms, shoulders, breasts, and stomach. You don't have to be unclothed for the kiss to have the desired effect. The proximity of a mouth against a body's limb, the scintillating sensation of feeling hot breath against your skin, add up to an extraordinary sensual touch.

The Knock Your Socks Off Kiss

A real good kisser won't be intimidated by convention. He'll take off those shoes and socks and kiss the ends of your toes, causing you to gasp uncontrollably.

The I've Got You Under My Skin Kiss

More audacious lovers know what the Europeans have always known, that the armpit is a luscious locale for planting passionate kisses. Nuzzle yourself inside the crook of her shoulder and drive her wild with ecstacy.

TOUCHY SUBJECTS

Congratulations. You've graduated to second base.

The expression "You rub me the right way" is music to my ears. One of the great pleasures of Terrific Sex is rediscovering the joys of petting. I had become so conditioned by the Sexual Revolution to think in terms of getting laid that I forgot what petting was all about. Oh, I was still doing it, but it was no longer an act unto itself. It was a step towards something else, a prerequisite to the big deed.

Today, I dote on petting. I thrive on it. Petting is a real turn-on. It's exploratory research with a kicker. Petting is what you do on a date when you slowly explore each other's bodies with your hands. Most of the time this is accomplished over clothing. But in the case of petting a girl's breasts this can include fondling underneath her brassiere. Gals can stroke a man's chest, run her fingers down his stomach, and eventually fondle his crotch. If he is erect, this can be quite a learning experience.

Masters and Johnson assert that petting is limited to stroking below the belt. That's news to me. I prefer to include the rest of the body simply because there's more to play with and I don't want to neglect anything.

To top it off, petting is a sensational way to get to know each other. There is time to simply enjoy the way a body feels taut and constricted within clothing. Sometimes the tantalizing spell cast by a bunched-up bit of fabric can be enough of a stimulus to provoke an unexpected orgasm.

FROTTAGE

Frottage (from the French verb *frotter* meaning "to rub") is a full-body, naked version of petting. When you lie on top of your nude lover and you're both grinding away at each other, you are indulging in frottage. It sounds fancy but it's really rather easy. It's also a hell of a lot of fun.

The pressure of one body lying on top of another lends a great deal to kissing. "Jane," a certified public accountant, told me how she loves it when she lies underneath her husband, feeling his full weight on top of her. "I like the feeling of being totally trapped, of feeling his hard hairy body pressing so close to me. I like to wrap my arms around his back and pull him even tighter, until neither of us can breathe."

Other women prefer to lie on top of their guy, feeling lighter, freer, and more in control. "Gretchen," a dancer, related how she likes to tickle her lover by sitting seductively on him, as he lies on his stomach. Slowly easing herself down his body, she starts from his neck along to his buttocks. "I particularly like sitting on his ass and stroking his back. I love to rub my pussy along his buttocks, creating friction against my clitoris. Sometimes, in this position, I have an orgasm."

Frottage can also be accomplished by "spooning" your body with your mate's. "Johnny," a strapping male model, related how once he was "caught in the act." It was during a photo shoot for a famous designer's cologne. "The art director made us take off all our clothes, and sit close to each other like we were in the throes of ecstacy. I remember I was sitting behind this incredibly sexy Oriental girl with very long silky black hair. My legs were wrapped around her legs. As the shoot got underway, I noticed she kept trembling next to me. I don't know if she was nervous or what, but pretty soon that little quiver was becoming an outright wiggle and I was getting a raging hard-on! Her hair, which was caught between us, was also doing a number on my cock. I was so embarrassed and the whole time the art director is telling us to squeeze closer together. I was worried that my lower extremity was going to show up in the ad photo! I tried thinking of terrible things—disasters, earthquakes, anything so horrible it would make me lose my erection. But I was completely at her mercy. She was tormenting me! When we were finished we separated and she turned her head over her shoulder and winked at me. I could have killed her! Later, I asked the photographer if he noticed anything peculiar in the pictures. I explained to him what had happened. He jokingly replied, "'Oh, that little thing, I wouldn't worry about it.'"

THE DRY HUMP

A rather negative way of expressing a positively enjoyable experience, the Dry Hump gets its undeserved arid name because the participants are usually fully clothed and there is no contact with bodily fluids. How fortunate! All the more reason these days to do it regularly. Positioned this way, the guy can rub his penis against the girl's vulva until he comes inside his pants. This can be embarrassing if it leaves a wet mark. But it's a reliable way to avoid exchanging bodily fluids.

Obviously the Dry Hump can be accomplished in a variety of ways. But try being different each time. Wear only underwear—or put a towel or a sheet between you. Satin is especially satisfying. Place a pillow between your loins and gently rock back and forth together. You may find that wearing bicycle shorts does the trick—or slip into some scuba gear. Experiment. Climaxes experienced in this manner can be some of the most excruciatingly delicious.

"Billy," a house painter who summers on Nantucket, recounted one "sexperience" that reminds me of the slang expression Cole Porter put to such good use in the musical *Anything Goes*: "She gives me *hot pants!*"

"It was a hot summer night," he explained, setting the scene. "My girlfriend, Suzy, and I had just come back from a picnic on the beach. She was wearing these itsy-bitsy faded white corduroy cutoffs. Anyway, Suzy said she couldn't stay over because she had to get to work real early the next morning. But just looking at her was getting me so horny. I told her to come and sit on my lap for a while before she left. We started to make out and it was fantastic! I could feel her pussy getting damp inside the cramped insides of her corduroy pants. She started to rub back and forth with her hips against my groin. My cock was rock hard inside my pants, stretching along the seam against my thigh. She straddled my knee and placed the ridges of her pussy lips directly on the head of my prick. Her clit was pressed against my shaft. Then she slowly rocked back and forth as we kissed, wiggling her cunt against me. I was going nuts! It felt so incredible. I dove my face between her tits and licked at them through her shirt. She started to bounce up and down on my legs, and I helped by meeting each one of her hip thrusts with more pressure from my thigh. Grabbing her, I clamped down on her mouth and eagerly bit her lip. I was coming—and from the way she was moaning, I knew she was too."

A RECIPE FOR SENSUAL MASSAGE

Polished practitioners of lovemaking, from the ancient authors of the *Kama Sutra* to modern-day sex surrogates, know that one of the simplest and most appealing ways of getting to know intimately your partner's body is through massage. If your boyfriend or husband, or girlfriend or wife, wants to immediately hit the hay, tell him or her you feel like giving them a back-rub first. Or if during a lazy afternoon, having finished mowing the lawn, you feel like a break, a sensual massage is a must.

The following is a rundown on the rubdown I love best. It's a simple approach to sexual relaxation. The overall effect stems more from the total concentration involved during the massage than from any actual muscular therapy. I leave that to shiatsu artists, professional masseurs, and able-bodied chiropractors.

First, turn on some soft sensual music minus the heavy bass line. You may find this on your Lite FM dial, or you can purchase "waterfall" music at most large record stores, new age health food emporiums, or your local spiritual bookshop.

Don't turn off the lights, and if you turn them

down leave enough illumination so that you can see his skin and body clearly. You may wish to put a scented handkerchief over a lamp (jasmine works beautifully), or insert a red, blue, or yellow light bulb instead of a bright white one. Pull out that old Lava Lamp you've stashed in the attic. I know some people who like to use a black light.

First of all, undress him until he's totally nude. Ask him to lie on his back. Put a hand towel or dry washcloth over his genitals if that makes him more comfortable. Some guys don't like to lie there with everything hanging out limp and exposed. But in no way should the body be confined or constricted.

Put a night mask or blindfold over his eyes. If you don't have one, use a face towel, neatly rolled in thirds.

Don't be too touchy at first. The secret to sensual massage is to get the person being massaged into a state where they are extremely sensitive to touch. A period of isolation prior to massage facilitates this transition. Leave his side for a moment and go to the other side of the room, or preferably into another room entirely. He's naked and vulnerable, and it's driving him crazy.

Come back in quietly. *Don't utter a word. Don't make a sound.* Take a little dab of lotion or massage oil and ever so slowly start rubbing it into the spaces between his toes. Gently rub them up and down, stroking each one inside your fist, your fingers, against the palm of your hands. The friction will create warmth.

Pretend each toe is his penis. He'll go nuts. If you like you can lick his toes, ease them individually into your mouth and suck them. Believe me, from my own experience, this is positively one of life's greatest pleasures.

Massage the arch of his foot, rub the sides as you

press into the softer middle section. Pull back the heel and press down on the pad below the toes. Give the foot a good stretch.

Now, slowly start up his calves. Most men are not aware of how crammed with sensitive nerve endings their calves are. If your mate is muscular or very athletic, his calves might be sinewy and taut. If he lives in a place with a lot of stairs, his calves will be crying out for some gentle love and attention. He'll love the way you're making him feel, and you'll adore the way his thick, hard leg muscles feel in your warm, creamy hands.

Gradually, after you've progressed up to his knees, you may wish to pull his legs apart and simply focus on one limb at a time. Lean over one leg and rub up and down from the base of the foot right up to the thigh. Knead it. It's tough. Giving a massage takes a lot of strength. Use both hands and stroke him firmly. Follow up with the other leg.

Now turn him over. Get him to lie face down on the mattress. If you can, it is important that the neck be limber, not strained. Letting the head hang over the end of the mattress can often alleviate this problem.

Start with the head this time around. Lightly massage the scalp, releasing pockets of tension under the hair. A number of people are extra-sensitive here, so be careful how fast and how forcefully you manipulate the skin. Gradually move down to the neck. Here you might want to pay extra-special attention, turning the head left and right. Don't try to crack the top of the spine. You can hurt him. The purpose of the massage is not to perform chiropractic therapy. You just want to relax him.

The shoulders are easy to manipulate, although because of their size, you might find yourself becoming fatigued. Your hands might begin to feel cramped, sore. Take a breather by lying down on top of him for a few seconds. Hold him to you. Lay your face against the smooth planes of his back.

When you're ready to continue, straddle his thighs just below his buttocks. Now you're about to begin the most important part of the massage. The lower back. This pocket of pent-up energy immediately above the tailbone and below the curve of the spine is the home of the "orgone," as Wilhelm Reich put it. By massaging this particular patch you are releasing positive vibes throughout his body. Everyone who has ever wanted to seduce someone through a backrub has known that manipulating the small of the back is the surefire way to give a guy a hard-on. He is totally at your mercy if you know how to do it right.

Again, flip him over. If all is going well, he will undoubtedly have an erection. Ignore it. Its appearance needn't divert you from your task at hand. Just concentrate on finishing the all-over massage.

Start to deeply rub the sides of his hips. Trace your fingers all along the outskirts of his genital area. If he grabs your hand and demands you stop, persevere and tell him you want to finish the job.

Move on to the abdomen, but be very careful since any undue pressure on the intestines can cause him discomfort and possibly pain.

Here you may wish to change positions and either come up from behind his head and start massaging from that vantage point, or climb aboard and straddle his hips, being careful not to let your bottom rub against his crotch. That can wait until the appropriate moment.

Skip ahead to his breasts. Cup your hands around his pectoral muscles. Flick your finger along his nipples. Press down on either side of his chest, squeezing his lateral muscles. Stroke his "lats" methodically.

Most men can't reach these muscles themselves and they are starved for affection. As you squeeze, press, and knead them, you will be releasing weeks worth of built-up tension. You are preparing his body for lovemaking, by freeing it from the bondage of pain.

Now move up to his shoulders and gradually spread both of your hands down along his upper arms and down past the elbows to his hands. Linger a while on the biceps and forearms. From eating chicken wings, you know how many little pockets of flesh and muscle there are in a limb. Feel his arm. Sense those areas that are keeping hold of locked-in pain . . . tension. Emancipate them!

When you get to his hands, spend a good amount of time toying with the muscles, bones, and joints. There are plenty of them, but persevere and do the best job you can. Once the hand is liberated, the whole body will be more limber. If you like, you can kiss, lick, nibble, and suck his fingers. Not only does this feel as good to him as having his penis sucked, but you might find yourself forgetting all about your earthly troubles. It's a simple, lovely pleasure. Enjoy.

Not only have you set the stage for some terrific lovemaking, but you've had a wonderful time yourself getting to know his body in the most personal way. Hopefully during your tour you've discovered nooks and crannies that are his particular erogenous zones. We all have our little secret spots, whether it's the back of the neck, under the arms, or somewhere along the thighs—it's best to find these little treasure troves of neglected nerve endings before you set out for the big bang. Now switch places. It's your turn.

THE SPIDER WEB

A woman's physique poses different problems for sensual massage. In general one doesn't have to cover as much territory since a woman's build is usually smaller than a man's. Here the male giving a woman an erotic rubdown has a distinct advantage over the woman doing the same to a man. His hands are so much bigger and stronger. Therefore, too, he has to be extra-careful not to over-massage or apply too much pressure.

I call this rubdown the Spider Web because the goal is to start from the four extremities (the tips of her outstretched hands to the tips of her spread feet) and gradually, by intricate design, work your way to the center, the hearth of the erogenous zones. This is where your fingers, working like little industrious spiders weaving across her body, will eventually entrap her into a stunning orgasm.

First ask her to lie down, nude, face down on the bed (or on a mattress on the floor). Take a dab of hand lotion and moisturize the weblike areas between her fingers. All ten of them! Softly, place your two hands over her hands and caress the fingers, allowing yours to fit snugly between each digit. Then inch them back so that the fleshy tips of your fingers are nestled at the pocket created at the very base of each joint. Apply just a little pressure, then gingerly trace your fingers along the top of her hand, sending little electrifying signals throughout her arms. Do this for a brief period, then slip your fingers back into the grooves of her fingers and grasp them tight. The feel of two moist hands clenching each other as you lie on top of her is very sensual indeed. Lean over and plant a few lustful kisses on each side of her soft, tender neck, making her break out into small groups of goose pimples.

Now, ease her arms apart. Not too hard. Just enough that she feels the tugging sensation at each shoulder and the release of tension built up in the wrists.

Okay. Change positions. Turn around and face her legs, all the while straddling her bottom. Apply more lotion to her sensitive little toes. Perform the same five finger exercises with her toes as you did with her fingers. Clutch each foot in your hand, massaging, soothing, slipping your fingers into the grooves of her toes. Ever so lightly pull her legs a few more inches apart.

Lean forward as you massage the arch of her feet. Allow your stomach and crotch to press into her buttocks. The pressure on her backside will release some of the tension carried in her lower spine, as well as titillate your genitals.

Continue up the legs, adding lubricant or oil when necessary. Massage and caress her calves, behind the knees, the base of her thighs.

Now we've arrived at the point of no return! A woman's thighs are extremely sensitive to touch. Don't bother with any cream here, you don't need it! The skin of a woman's thighs is one of the softest materials on earth. Delicate puffs of cotton in your thick strong hands. Lightly trace your fingers up and down her thighs. If you like you can use a feather or a flannel cloth, and gently pass it along the contours of the inner thighs. Don't be surprised if she flexes and flinches. Continue the careful attention. Press down on both thighs from the top and work the muscle down to the knee. Keep doing this until you feel her legs melting like butter in your hands.

This part of the massage completed, you'll want to change positions again and pay some attention to her shoulders. Turn around and begin to rub her back muscles just below and to the sides of the neck. Because of their charm-school posture, women carry a great deal of tension here. And as the Japanese know only too well, a woman's neck is an erogenous zone in its own right. Soothe her. Stroke her. Make love to her with your hands! Allow her to get rid of the pain, to become putty in your hands. What could be more arousing than to be free from any worries or tension?

Move down a bit to the side muscles of the back. Press down gently and push to each side, unlocking pockets of hidden tension. Continue the parting motions until she begins to squirm contentedly beneath you.

That's your cue to flip her over.

Kneeling between her legs, facing her upper body, continue massaging her arms back and forth from the fingers to the shoulders. Then sweep down and lightly smooth your palms over her breasts. Even if they are large, don't exert too much pressure. The breast is very sensitive to touch and doesn't respond well to squeezing, pushing, or pounding. Slip your fingers along the underside of the breasts, then cup your hand around the mound. Let go. Brush your hand along the nipple, spinning the heart of your palm against the sensitive tip.

After a few go-arounds, drop your hands to her rib cage and trace the muscles leading from her chest to her abdomen. Here you will want to concentrate a few minutes on the crucial hip area. In women, the hips get a lot of action. They're constantly being used in walking, bending, carrying, standing, and if she's smart, wiggling. Pay as much attention to her hips as you would her breasts. Use your thumb to rub out the trapped pockets of tension, kneading the flesh here with fervent, commanding motions.

When you've fully liberated the muscles here, slide your hands down both outer surfaces of her thighs, almost as if, in leaning forward, you're hugging her.

Now lift her legs by picking up each foot and ever so gently pushing the leg back towards the body, bending at the knee. Do this several times, then lift the foot and place her calves over each shoulder. Lean down so that her legs are not unnecessarily too high. The lifting motion will provide a rush of blood to her vulva, as well as her head. Slightly dizzy, flushed, warm, she will want you to touch her where it feels the best—in the heart of her loins.

PRINCIPLE 9

DECENT EXPOSURE

Catherine Deneuve was once asked how she keeps her face so clean. She said the secret to washing one's face was to start with clean hands.

Similarly, it is important in Terrific Sex that you start out right with proper hygiene. This you can achieve for yourself, but you can't always be sure that your new friend is one hundred percent a-okay. That's why a little decent exposure is a must.

One simple yet valuable way to get a good look at your lover's body prior to having sex is to take a shower or a bath beforehand.

I don't know about you, but I've always thought bathrooms are incredibly sexy. I love the shiny quality of the tiled walls and floor, the glimmering porcelain of the toilet and bathtub. The voluptuous feel of terry cloth towels, and the fleshlike rubberized sensation of shower curtains and bathmats. The bathroom is a cornucopia of imaginative sexual playthings.

SEXY SHOWERS

Showers have always been refreshing, and it doesn't take a genius to see that if you rinse together you might enjoy it twice as much. In the film *The Italian Stallion*, starring a grumpy but very nude Sylvester Stallone, there is a long languorous scene in which Sly, playing a gigolo, takes a shower with his bossy, big-breasted ladyfriend. I found this scene the most erotic one in the movie because of the atmosphere of exploration and tenderness projected by the two actors. At one point Stallone grabs a bar of soap and massages her voluminous breasts with his massive rough hands. They are both obviously very aroused by the sudsy horseplay.

Soap is great because it allows you to glide along the body, working as a slick friction buster and a temporary lubricating device. While under the pulsating spray of the shower, you can reach around and slip your fingers inside the warm spot created by the union of the two buttocks, then glide right along the perineum.

The shower provides a perfect opportunity to get a really close-up look at your partner's genitals. For instance, ladies, while you are soaping up your lover's erogenous zone, stroke his penis with your slippery fingers. Make sure you use a soap that doesn't have any strong deodorants since these can aversely affect the urethra and cause irritating stinging. Feel how easily your digits slide across the skin of his shaft. Once you reach the tip of his penis, make a fist and quickly spin your hand around his glans. Now, sweep back down to his testicles. As he becomes erect, you can keep your eye on his foreskin, if he has one. Pull it back far enough to completely expose the glans. This is your moment to check to see if it is clean, free from any sores, abrasions, or disturbing looking discharges.

Case in point. One woman told me of an experience she had while having sex with a young man who happened to be a dancer at Chippendale's. She discovered a miniscule "arch" growing on the tip of his penis. She was really taken aback, and was afraid to continue fondling him. She was afraid of this little bump with a hole in it on the edge of his glans. She couldn't help asking him what it was. He told her it was the hole through which he put his "cockring," not the type of cockring that guys fit around their shaft and testicles to increase their virility, but an earring that he wore on his penis. He was the first guy she'd ever met who had had his phallus pierced!

So it pays to take the time to fully look at what you're holding in your hands. It also makes sense to inquire if you come across anything out of the ordinary.

STEAMY BATHS

Just as showers come in handy before sex, so do hot baths. Depending on the size of your tub, there are various options for bubbly fun. If the two of you can fit into the basin, you may wish to turn on a radio, light some candles, burn some incense, and lie in the warm invigorating waters together. Smell is one of the most powerful aphrodisiacs. You may wish to try bubble bath that is scented, or release a few drops of your favorite perfume into the water and let it cast a fragrant aura around you.

The point is—have fun! Take the tension out of the air by relaxing and letting go.

More ambitious lovers may wish to buy a whirlpool device from your local hardware or department store. These removable items are not terribly expensive and they are very relaxing. If you really want to go all out, spring for a Jacuzzi, and pretty soon you'll be whirring yourself into a blistering, spectacular romantic frenzy.

SHOWER HEAD

While you're in the tub, showering or bathing, why not take advantage of the erotic charms of a WaterPik showerhead. These devices create a potent jet with a fierce trajectory that sends a shooting stream of hot water onto your skin. Maneuver it so that it hits your breasts, buttocks, clitoris, or penis.

THE BIDET

Most American households are still not outfitted with a bidet, a standard in Europe. These devices are toilet-shaped sinks constructed low on the floor and on which a man or woman can rinse his or her private parts. The bidet is a sensational locale for masturbation, mutual or solo, and a fountainhead of sensible hygiene. Since a bidet has both hot and cold streams of water, some of which shoot up from the bowl onto the genitals, it offers direct stimulation that can be as fascinating to watch as it is to have it done to you.

Once you've finished in the bathroom, or if you weren't able to get to one, there are other methods of revealing foreplay that can keep you clean.

HOT LIGHTS

Since most people are embarrassed about sex, and afraid of intimacy, they prefer to have sex with the lights off, or in a room where the illumination is so muted that the room resembles a morgue rather than a bordello.

These days if you want to get the most out of sex, you have to be willing to shed some light on the situation.

116

TORCH SONG

Some women I know find flashlights to be very erotic. First of all they are often shaped like a penis, and that penetrating beam of light is awfully evocative of a scandalously long orgasm.

When you and your lover undress and he insists on leaving the lights off, maybe because he's shy or maybe because he's uptight about his body, go along with him and then surprise him by turning on a flashlight. The limited amount of space that is lit up by a flashlight provides you with a moving spotlight.

Shine the beacon momentarily on his face. Hold it under your own and show him that you're smiling. Be playful. Start pinpointing parts of his body that appeal to you. Place the flashlight under each of your breasts, along your thighs, under his balls. You'll be delighted to discover that your simple motions are getting him very turned on.

Point the light directly on his penis. Tell him how beautiful it looks in the limelight. He will respond to the heat of the torch by becoming even more inspired. Touch him and gently stroke his testicles and penis as you explore. If he is uncircumcised, now is your chance to pull back his foreskin and see the marvelous shape of his corona.

Give him the light and let him titillate you, gazing at the variety of folds and dimples that comprise your sex. Once and for all you'll disprove that old "husband's tale" that in the dark they are all the same.

HOT WAX

What can be more beautiful than making love by candlelight? How about making love *with* candlelight? Whenever I'm feeling especially passionate, I take a candle to bed with me. Bringing a lit candle to bed can be dangerous, obviously, if you drop it on the sheets. But if you're careful, you can manipulate the candle over your partner's body, dropping little dollops of wax on his skin. This is rarely painful. Plus, you have the added bonus of seeing things more clearly.

THE ULTRA TAN

I know one gentleman who can't stop thinking about sex when he's lying under an ultraviolet light at his tanning salon. One time, he confessed, he masturbated into the towel he was given. To him and others out there, I suggest the following. Why not outfit your bathroom with a tanning light, or purchase a free-standing model and place it in your bedroom to help you get more comfortable with your partner prior to sex. This way if you do make love you can get a tan at the same time. Just remember to wear goggles and put the timer on.

PRINCIPLE 10

HOW TO MAKE LOVE TO ONESELF

THE SECRETS OF SOLO SEX

Masturbation has been called one of the saviors of the human race! Mark Twain called it "the fundamental sigh." And there is no question that in these difficult days, autoeroticism provides a simple solution to sexual desire. It is surely the safest way to have sex without risking AIDS—and since it provides self-love, self-expression, and self-exploration, it also encourages better mental health. Yet for many adults solo sex still connotes childish behavior, loneliness, sexual immaturity, and frustration. It is still commonly, and erroneously, referred to as self-abuse.

For me, autoeroticism is a joyful experience. I even use it as a form of meditation. Betty Dodson, whose book *Self-Love & Orgasm* has become the bible of confirmed masturbators, agrees wholeheartedly. "Masturbation represents our primary sex life," she told me. "It constitutes our sexual base."

Self-stimulation allows for splendid, all-encompassing orgasms without any of the worry or anxiety that accompany other forms of sex. In many ways, the sexual release achieved by autoeroticism is more satisfying. Masters and Johnson came to the conclusion that the "corpus contraction patterns" induced by masturbatory manipulation were of greater intensity and duration than those brought on by intercourse. Kinsey documented one woman who was able to have one hundred orgasms in the space of an hour by self-stimulation. Perhaps this is why the Viennese critic Karl Klaus insisted that "coitus is but a weak substitute for masturbation." Oscar Wilde was an advocate of masturbation as well. He argued that it was "cleaner, more efficient, and you meet a better class of person."

David Cole Gordon, in his book *Self-Love* (MacMillan, 1968), believes masturbation is a "unification experience" that is "so profoundly satisfying not just because man becomes one with himself, but also because he becomes one with the world and others, and for that brief moment of eternity all of his earthly problems are resolved." One young man referred to his masturbatory orgasm as "a fantastic moment of freedom!" What a marvelous way to deal with your anxieties and frustrations regarding AIDS!

But not only that. Masturbation is the key to unlocking the loving person inside of you ready and willing to be a Terrific Sex partner.

THE TIME FACTOR

The first secret of solo sex is—don't rush it! Give yourself time to indulge in the plethora of sensations at your disposal. Rome wasn't built in a day, nor was a mind-blowing orgasm accomplished in thirty seconds.

Don't pull down your pants or hike up your skirt at the drop of a hat and expect to find nirvana when you only have five minutes. Masturbation should never be something that you want to get out of the way, like doing the laundry. If you have a busy schedule, make an appointment. Set aside an hour during the day when you can take the phone off the hook, and be totally alone, in peace, without any interruptions. While you make love to yourself, you are otherwise engaged.

Dally with all your erogenous zones. Try and keep the focus off simply coming. The reason it's called a climax is that it comes at the end of a long, exhilarating dramatic play. Let all of your anatomical characters have their moment in the footlights. Don't rush to oblivion. An orgasm will feel a thousand times more orgasmic if you have nurtured it well. Keep it guessing. Tease it mercilessly. To paraphrase George Bernard Shaw, pleasure is most exquisite when it comes after a prolonged painful period of postponement.

Follow the model of "Hedda," a Florida hairstylist who prefers to devote a half hour to an hour of each evening just as she's preparing for bed, watching late night movies, reading, talking to friends on the phone, all the while caressing herself, bringing on a rich, rewarding climax. "I also like to lay back in the bathtub, with just enough water to keep me warm, and rub myself for the longest time, letting my mind wander, and my thought patterns drift off. All sorts of things come to mind, but I don't linger on any one. I whiz through a series of sexy pictures, while twirling my fingers in and around my vagina. When I come I kiss my arms and breasts, tasting the dewlike drops of sweat that have formed." Hedda claims she's never experienced insomnia since she's mastered this trick.

"Charlie" is an investment banker living in Brooklyn Heights, New York. He finds masturbation to be beneficial in terms of his work. "When I'm under a great deal of pressure," he shared with me, "or if I need to calm down from too much excitement, I find solace in playing with myself. I'm not married, and sometimes I just don't want to share my feelings with another person. I prefer to be alone. At such times, I pull down all the shades in the living room, and take out my 'dirty' magazines and spread them out on the floor. Then I strip down until I'm naked and I move all around the room, looking at the centerfolds from different perspectives. I especially like to look at a pair of tits upside down. I continue to jerk off for about an hour. By then I'm so excited that I almost have blueballs and my prick is rock hard. When I finally come, it's tremendous. I shoot all over the place, and eventually collapse back on the couch, heaving a happy sigh of relief. The next day I'm totally refreshed and ready to go back to work."

LUBRICATION

Sometimes in masturbation, the body doesn't secrete enough natural lubrication. Saliva is a popular emollient, and Dr. Alex Comfort, the author of *The Joy Of Sex*, recommends it as the "best lubricant." I disagree. The mouth is full of more germs than any of the sexual orifices, and spit should not be used even on yourself.

Try natural oils like vegetable oil, olive oil, peanut oil, sesame oil, and sunflower oil. Soap is widely used but as I previously stated the chemical ingredients in certain soaps can irritate the urethra. For a man, this can ruin a potentially terrific orgasm. The cosmetic and pharmaceutical industries market thousands of products, from baby oil to KY Jelly, that can safely be used in masturbation. Some like Vaseline Intensive Care Lotion and Lubriderm are unreasonably expensive. One perennial favorite is a concoction known as rose milk which has a delightful consistency and a tendency not to be too quickly absorbed into the skin. There is nothing worse than being close to climax and finding yourself high and dry.

That is why Astrolube, Inc. has come up with the incredible lubricant ASTROGLIDE, "the intimate lubricant formulated to ease and enhance every sexual pleasure." Researching the "contributive causes of sexual orgasm," the makers of ASTROGLIDE discovered that women who use birth control pills, or those who have passed through menopause, have difficulty in producing an adequate amount of lubrication. According to the promotional material, "over eighty percent of the obstetrician/gynecologists contacted during a test-marketing period are now recommending ASTROGLIDE to their patients." Likewise, men need a secondary source of lubrication in order to ensure that they don't rub themselves raw. This product is odorless, colorless, non-staining, flavorless, and made of "thixotropic gelation agents, emollients, humectants, purified (deionized) water, stabilizers, and a mild preservation system designed to preclude reaction to the more sensitive areas of the body. The pH of the system is slightly acidic, so as to match the natural balance of the body . . . this results in decreased viscosity of the gel, reducing any sheer force. The formulation uses a long-chain, nonabsorbent, water-soluble, polymeric material as the gelation agent."

What does all this mean? Listen to how one user

describes its benefits. "It's so good it's almost inde-
scribable! I'm male, and I use it for masturbation and I
must say . . . in terms of direct stimulation, it's better
than being inside most women I've known. Yes, really!
When I use ASTROGLIDE, my organ becomes so hard
it feels like something separate from my body . . . I go
totally crazy and lose my cool."

And a female fan: "Having over the years run the
whole gamut of Vaseline, KY, Albolene, various hand
lotions, and on one occasion of urgent ecstacy, mayon-
naise, I must tell you that nothing remotely measures
up to your product. Not only is it a breeze in terms of
cleanup, but it offers sensational staying power as
well. . . ."

An extra-special thrill of ASTROGLIDE is that it
can be used in all forms of sexual activity, and works
beautifully with condoms. If you can't find any AS-
TROGLIDE at your local "sex shoppe," write to Astrolube, Inc., P.O. Box 9788, North Hollywood, Ca. 91609,
or call 1-818-989-1136.

Meanwhile, use your imagination. A friend of
mine told me about a trip he made to his grand-
mother's house. Late at night he got the urge to masturbate but he couldn't find any type of lotion
anywhere in the house. And he wasn't quite up to asking her. Eventually he stumbled into the kitchen hoping to find a bottle of vegetable oil, or even, if he had
to, a can of Crisco. Instead all he could get his hands
on was a bottle of corn syrup! In no mood to miss out
on a much-needed orgasm, my friend tried the corn
syrup and found, much to his surprise, that it worked
superbly. Other impromptu gourmet lubricants include margarine, butter, peanut butter, whipped
cream, and the long-standing popular choice, honey.

As usual, mind your ABCs—the building blocks of
sensible sex. Don't experiment with lotions or liquids

that don't provide lubrication. Creme rinses and conditioners might resemble semen, in terms of their consistency and color, but they make lousy lubricants. Avoid any products with glue in them. I heard one horror tale of a young man who reached behind him once when he was masturbating in order to squeeze out some Jergens lotion from a pump dispenser. He applied a thick cream to his penis. The nightmare was that he had pressed down on the wrong dispenser and was actually putting Liquid Sew, a very strong type of glue, on his penis. Luckily he was able to wash it off before it solidified. Don't be foolhardy. Who knows, you may end up putting "vanishing creme" on yourself by accident.

ANAL EROTICISM

Too often solo sex is limited to mere genital play. Many self-stimulators attest to the perennial appeal of the anal pore. Don't be embarrassed to plumb its wonders yourself. Tickling the sensitive ridges of the anus can offer terrific sexual excitement to you, male or female. The male sex has the "Oh-gee!" Spot, or prostate gland, and therefore an added bonus in anal stimulation. Women don't have a prostate, but some have questioned whether the mysterious G-Spot might not be a first cousin of the prostate. Stimulation of the anus in females is one way of further exciting this all-important erogenous zone.

While masturbating, why not press the fat part at the base of your thumb up against the perineum, and massage the area surrounding the anus. Later, if you wish, you can gently insert a finger inside your rectum. Not too far, at first, until you are comfortable with deeper penetration. (NOTE: Please make sure you check to see that your finger is clean, and that your nails are adequately clipped. No sharp edges or devices should ever be placed within the anus. Here, our slogan "Out of Body, Out of Mind" would also apply. For safety's sake, don't put anything that could slip out of your hands inside you.)

SEX TOYS!

Is there anyone who hasn't admitted to a curious fascination with sex toys? Many of these erotic gadgets come in handy during masturbation. For women there are dildos, ben-wa's, and the infamous vaginal inserts favored by French tarts called "pommes d'amour." But the simplest and most efficient sex toy is the vibrator.

The Thrill of Vibrators

Vibrators have always been an invaluable tool in self-stimulation because they offer a unique sensation not possible in other forms of sexual manipulation. Therefore, inspired inventors have come up with a panoply of products to enhance your (not to mention, their) masturbatory sessions.

There's a new contraption called the Butterfly that straps snugly over a woman's "hot spot" to "provide wave after wave of orgasmic pleasure!" which "operates so quietly you can even wear it under your clothes!"

Do you prefer to be treated roughly? Then get your hands on the Thumper—a "professional-size nine-inch-long hard-rubber vibro-ball with variable speed and vibration settings." As the ad campaign reveals "not only does this professional model give truly soothing deep-muscle massages but when you apply the head to pussy and clitoris, you'll enjoy an absolute earthquake of orgasm-stimulating vibrations." How about the Fill 'Er Up! "A full two inches thick with an even larger base that tortures your labia and clitoris" plus "eight inches of lifelike penetration!" Finally, there's the Hot Stud Vibrator that comes equipped with a special "accordion flex" tip that thrusts while it shakes, rattles and rolls, but also gets "HOT!" so it slides in without the "usual chill."

Men are beginning to experience the thrill of electric stimulators too. Planting the tip of a vibrator at the edge of the corona, or at the base of the shaft is sometimes a great notion. Leaving it on the perineum while you masturbate is even better. Easing the head of a vibrator into the opening of the anus is an asset to any autoerotic session.

"Peter," a thirty-nine-year-old veterinarian and a widower, related his first masturbatory experience, which involved a hand massager. "I was twelve, I think, and I remember using my father's hand massager one afternoon when he was out. I started rubbing my arms, neck, and chest—and eventually ended up placing the vibrating massager against my crank. It felt real good—so I left it there. After a few minutes, I started to shake and this gooey white stuff came out of my dick. I was so scared, I threw the hand massager away. It was so funny because for weeks afterward my father looked around the house, saying, 'Has anyone seen my hand massager!' Now that I'm a grownup myself, and a father, I wonder if my father was using the hand massager the same way I did?"

Since then, Peter has collected an array of massaging devices that satisfy his libido. One, in particular, a hand-held "vibro-massage" unit, does the trick. "My favorite way to jerk off is to lay in bed with the lights on low, listening to some old Motown records, and flipping through some old nudie magazines. I put the vibro-massage between my thighs and hold it against my balls. That way I can turn the pages of the magazines with one hand, and stroke myself with the other."

Household Items

You can also experiment with choice sex gadgets readily available in every home. Hot water bottles, bathing caps, douche bags, and large fruits or vegetables. "Jackie," a playwright who lives outside Greenwich, Connecticut, is unabashed about her love of vegetarianism. She likes to masturbate with a cucumber. "I leave it under the hot water from my sink for a couple of seconds, making it nice and warm. Then I take the cucumber to bed with me. The first time I tried it, I thought I was going to die laughing. What if someone saw me? But now it's become a regular part of my routine. It's safe. Clean. And wonderful fun! And I never have to worry about shopping for the right size. I grow my own in the backyard."

Enemas

Mention the word enema and a lot of people grimace. They think of antiseptic hospital rooms and large tubes. But enemas can be used safely, and quite productively during sexual relations. First, if you are planning to indulge in an hour or two of anal eroticism, an enema can help you prepare the rectum hygenically for penetration and massage. Second, just the feeling of being full of water is for many people a thoroughly delightful experience, one that adds an extra boost to their orgasms. Men find that it stimulates their prostate (most men get an erection when given an enema). Women find that it stimulates the vagina by virtue of its proximity. One important point. An enema should not be used as a wash prior to anal sex with another person. It has been shown that an enema actually depletes the rectum of its natural protective germs. But in terms of autoeroticism, it is a harmless touch.

Have you ever experienced the amazing BARDEX TUBE? This illustrious gadget is an enema unit, shaped like a two-headed turkey baster. One squeeze bulb fits inside your sphincter and expands as you pump air into it by squeezing the other. Meanwhile, warm water cascades throughout your rectum. The Bardex is not recommended to those without a little time on their hands.

Brushfire

Now is the time to take advantage of that electric toothbrush you've shoved towards the back of your medicine cabinet. The electric toothbrush has been underrated as an erotic aid. Attach a brush that you don't use on your teeth, and press the tip of the throbbing electric device against some part of your body, whether it's the penis, the perineum, the clitoris, or the mons veneris. This little vibrator is a surefire way to lend a touch of whimsy to any masturbatory session.

High-Tech Devices

For those of you who prefer Father Science to Mother Nature, dedicated inventors and ingenious engineers have come up with a variety of clever contrivances to facilitate mechanical autoeroticism. Take your pick among a litany of contraptions.

The Blow-up Doll functions very well the first time around, but is very difficult to keep clean. It is available in a variety of shapes, sizes and physiques, as well as sexual inclinations. Ladies can choose the Playguy, a male doll that is "so strong, so firm, so flexible." It has a "fleshlike vinyl body," stands a full six feet tall, has all male parts built in, a fully detailed face with mustache. "He will submit to your every whim. He never says no!" As an ad for the Playguy insists, "Don't take chances! Have safe sex with your very own love slave!" There's one Playguy named "Greg" who's endowed with a number of attractive features. "All of his male components are built right into his body. His large masculine chest, strong molded legs, finely detailed face. You can even control his size. Make Greg thin, make him husky, or just plain muscular." Plus you can dress him up. "Greg can wear regular men's clothing. His strong legs can wear boots or shoes. Dress him like a cowboy. Dress him in sports clothes. He can wear anything from a bathing suit to a tuxedo." The professional model, which costs $59.95, has a special ejaculating feature!

The Oro-Simulator, designed for men, is another

fancy sex toy. A plastic cap that fits tightly over the top of the penis (it's measured according to your personal dimensions), the Oro-Simulator "strokes up and down your penis all by itself" and is "completely portable." It "slides wetly, smoothly up and down, even screws crazily, wildly, round and round. Like the best blow job and the wildest fuck you ever had or imagined!"

There's also the highly-touted Mouth, a masturbation device that fits like a sheath over the entire penis. "This baby doesn't look like much," the ad announces, "but wow!!! When you squeeze out the air, the sides collapse on you like loving cheeks and tongue. As you pull, it sucks, sucks, SUCKS!"

Many of you might have already heard of the JAC-PACK. This inflatable sleeve fits over the penis like a glove (but looks like a life preserver that a child wears over his arm). "No other male masturbation aid can compare!" its makers assure us. "So close to 'the real thing' you'll think it's alive!"

Both of you might find the VIOLETTA to be a triumph of modern science. No, this is not a recording of Renata Tebaldi singing *La Traviata*, it's a much more exotic offering. The Violetta is a glass tube (packaged in a velvet-lined box that resembles a clarinet's carrying case) that when plugged into a socket sends out a titillating electrical impulse and lights up with an eerie, astonishing purple glow. Users should know what they're doing before they plug in this electrical device. But when pressed against the flesh (as far away from the bathtub as possible!) it shocks, tickles, and ultimately devastates. Ouch! It feels really fantastic against one's nipples or underneath one's testicles, anywhere you've got some gooseflesh.

None of these devices, however, can compare with the thrill-of-a-lifetime, the world-famous ACCU-JAC machine. (Also available from Funways, Inc.)

Playboy magazine has called it "the apex of sexual technology." The original ACCU-JAC (which can cost as much as $250.00) is composed of a plastic sleeve that slides over the penis connected to a plastic tube that is attached to a motor. This boxlike motor creates an incredible vacuum simulating intercourse. "Simultaneously, airflows which breathe in and out play upon the penis just like oral stimulation . . . from gentle suction to power stroking, from a teasing fondle to a hungry, demanding drive!"

The ACCU-JAC Companion Model is designed for female massage, outfitted with a "ruggedly built, beautifully designed, and fully warranted" bellows-type dildo that is held between the legs, as it slides in and out of the vagina. "Escape to a world of erotic dreams while the Companion makes them real!" The brochure exclaims "American women have discovered an alternative to the chemical world of tranquilizers and alcohol. Over forty percent now use massaging aids of some type, and of all such devices, the Companion is King."

The ACCU-JAC II is designed for both males and females. As Funways sees it, "Humankind is unique in the animal kingdom; 24 hours a day, 365 days a year, we are in heat. The pursuit of sexual fulfillment is an endless and costly game. Now, ACCU-JAC II changes all that." The External mode powers a clear, pliant sheath, sliding up and down, subtly coaxing the fullest erection, and providing the most erotic sensations. The Internal mode "gently powers an amazingly lifelike erect penis."

As one fan put it, "The ACCU-JAC is easily the greatest invention since the wheel. I have had one for three months and don't know how I existed without it. Now I need a second unit for my vacation home."

What do you think? Is there an ACCU-JAC in your future?

PRINCIPLE II

A JOINT EFFORT

THE MERITS OF MUTUAL MASTURBATION

Once you become an aficionado of solo sex, there's no question that you become a better lover. The Boston Women's Health Book Collective has claimed that "masturbating can exist as a useful part of a person's sexual development. Besides helping you learn to enjoy your body, it can also teach you what techniques prove best for arousing yourself, so that you can show your sexual partner how to arouse you."

Think of the abundance of techniques you've just mastered that you can now happily apply to mutual masturbation and manual lovemaking. This is the one time that manipulation in a relationship is wholeheartedly endorsed.

Before we can get into the nitty-gritty of duo-eroticism, I think it would be best to study the basics of manual technique. Most men I spoke with feel that women aren't skilled at handling penises. Their grips are too limp, lacking conviction and exuberance. They seem afraid to apply pressure, and yet often pull or tug at inappropriate moments, disrupting the rhythm that is so important. They also have a tendency to scratch.

Clearly, we all need to be more knowledgeable about the proper methods of mutual masturbation. Men, it would help if you knew the proper directions to give. And women, you can surprise your boyfriends by mastering the techniques on your own.

TIPS ON THE PERFECT HAND JOB

The following exercises can be performed by whomever is doing the stroking—either you or your partner. But it is written with the woman in mind, especially if she is not well acquainted with the object at hand.

Your first concern will always be the matter of size. Is it large or small? Somewhere in between? No issue has received greater attention than the size of a man's penis. Ninety percent of the time, it's the male of the species who spends his time making wishes under "the bridge of size." Since men invariably judge each other's virility by the length of their phalli, every locker room resounds with the sound of catcalls and whistles that result when a guy passes by boldly unveiling his enviable equipment. It's left to women to try and console those guys who have been congenitally shortchanged. Man's obsession with genital size is probably a mental vestige of his primitive primate past, but as far as human sexuality is concerned, it's a waste of time. A large penis doesn't have any effect on a woman's physical enjoyment, unless it's too big or unless she has a deep-seated psychological attachment to well-endowed men.

How about its shape? Remember you vowed to be there through thick and thin. Is it curved like a boomerang, or is it straight as an arrow? Does your fist fit around the spongy mass of the shaft? Does your hand completely engulf it? This is good because you can squeeze all of it at once. But don't be an organ-grinder. Be gentle, yet firm. If the penis has an unusual girth, your hand may not completely encircle it. In such cases, try both hands to ensure you don't miss any of the tender areas while stroking.

Explore every square inch of his genital surface area. Men love to have their penises worshiped, played with, tickled, fondled, massaged. Let him know that you are not afraid, or ashamed, or disinterested in finding out everything there is to know about his crotch. Most men don't even know how sensitive they really are down there. Show him that you do.

Don't start stroking or jerking quite yet. Just feel the fullness of it all. Let your fingers run from the balls up to the top of the cockhead, swirl around there for a bit, then slide back down the other half and end back down at the testicles. The movements should be swift and smooth, without bumping or stalling.

Now, you're ready for some stepped-up action, but you don't want to suddenly lapse into a series of beatings, whackings, jackings, and jerkings. Tease the more sensitive areas of his penis. These include: the glans and the tender part on the bottom side of his penis.

Bring your palm up to the top of the glans and park it there flat out, fingers held together and stiff, thumb pointed straight out. Spin it around as if you were trying desperately to remove the recalcitrant lid of a jar. Your man will be groaning in delicious agony. The corona is supersensitive and this motion sends little shivers of exquisite pleasure througout his being. He might grimace and cry out, and possibly try to push your hand away, but he's loving every second of it. Now's your chance to be the one who plows ahead even though he's pleading with you to stop!

After you've done that for a bit, slip your hand down to his testicles and ever-so-gently hold them in your fingers, softly tugging them down away from his shaft. If they are big and bulky, like Grade AA eggs, bounce them up and down a couple of times in your hand. Tell him how hot they feel, how sexy they are. Whatever you do, don't squeeze them! This could put a real damper on your lovemaking for the rest of the day. You might notice that one of his nuts hangs lower than the other. This is perfectly normal. Once you feel comfortable with the way his balls feel in your hand gently roll them up the underside of his shaft. Depending on their size and the amount of room in the scrotum, they will most likely reach up to half of his penis. He will like the way this feels.

Now, let go of his testicles and bring your fingers together in a makeshift goosehead formation. Very lightly, begin to stroke his erection with your fingers, running them all over his sensitive shaft and balls. You may wish to slip the pocket of your goosehead handhold over the tip of his penis, letting it rest there for a few seconds.

If all is going well, the penis will probably start to emit its natural lubricant. Pre-seminal fluid is nature's way of moistening the canal of the urethra so that the spermatozoa can swim more easily out of it, as well as lubricating the head of the penis. Uncircumcized penises gather up this lubricant within the foreskin and keep the head very moist and slick. Use the juice to lubricate the shaft. Sometimes there is a musky smell that can be an aromatic aphrodisiac for you both.

A Joint Effort

If there is little or no pre-cum, don't be concerned. It is not a requirement and does not always appear at exactly the same time.

In any case a good lubricant will work just as well in mutual masturbation as it does in autoeroticism. Add a drop of moisturizing lotion to the shaft and gently rub it in. Alexandra Penny, in her book *How To Make Love To A Man*, is very keen on massaging the lotion between one's hands before putting it on the penis. Sometimes the cream is cold and the palm rubbing warms it up.

ASTROGLIDE succeeds exceptionally well here. Cara Lott, an X-rated movie star, has stated that "when I'm being intimate on a movie set with a camera crew and thirty technicians watching, you can bet your booties lubrication can be a problem. I find AS-TROGLIDE is so similar to a man and woman's own natural lubrication that sometimes during a film shoot my partner and I forget we're only acting."

If your partner doesn't seem to have a very firm erection, try using a cinnamon-based ointment that you can find at your local sex novelty store, or acquire through a mail catalog. The slight burning sensation often causes the penis to become rock hard. Adding a little dab to the testicles also helps. If you really want to do a number on him, slip a bit of Ben-Gay on his balls and watch him go through the roof.

As previously noted, one of the secrets of solo sex is varying your hand motions. Here are a few techniques that I think are indispensable.

Switch-Hitter

Use both hands, alternating back and forth in a pattern you develop to offer him the most arousal. He will notice the difference. Your less practiced hand is more tentative, less firm. He'll respond to that. But only temporarily. Don't get into a routine where the strokes are dull, and noncommittal. Give it to him good. Get him to the point where he's singing out, "I second that hand motion!"

Double Whammy

How about going double or nothing! Bring both well-lubricated hands down on his shaft. Some cocks are so big they require two hands. If your partner's doesn't, then use the other hand to caress and lightly flutter his balls, or tighten around the base of his shaft. If both hands fit along the length of the shaft, move them together, up and down, in the typical pumping motion. Pretend you're holding a baseball bat and are about to score a grand slam. You can also vary the directions of your hands, one up, one down at the same time. There's no doubt that in such a situation two hands are better than one.

The Anvil Stroke

Bring one hand down, letting it stroke the penis from the top all the way to the bottom. When it hits the bottom release it. Meanwhile you're bringing your corresponding hand down to the top of the shaft, creating an alternating beating motion, hence the name anvil stroke. Think of those blacksmith duos who keep up a double-beat pounding motion as they beat that rod of iron on a piping hot anvil.

A Joint Effort

The Shuttle Cock

Not many people have heard of the Shuttle Cock hand motion but it's one of the best. Take the penis in both hands, fingers lightly touching the sides of the shaft. In order to visualize the position, think of yourself holding a clarinet. Now flick the penis back and forth between your two hands by holding on to the loose skin of the shaft. Shuttling it back and forth in this manner may not seem incredibly thrilling to him at first, but pretty soon as it builds up momentum, it will drive him out of his mind. Orgasms encountered via this method are sometimes messy, but always memorable.

The Bookends

Place both of your hands side by side against his shaft like a pair of bookends. Now push hard against his penis. Then lift your hands up and down. Continue in this manner for a while. The constant tugging on the skin around the balls and the mons pubis will do the trick, bringing this bookworm to a finish that is literally sensational.

The Flame

Place your hands down on either side, your fingers pointing away from the cock. Pretend you're a campfire girl and start spinning his pecker like a stick of wood. This way you'll keep the home fires burning for a long time to come.

The Slapstick

For members only, this is a trick passed on to me by a high-class female escort. When giving a hand job, slap the penis. Not too hard, of course. You don't want to hurt anybody, but hit him hard enough that the penis throbs for a second in pain. This technique is especially useful in reviving fading stiffs, or poking fun at the odd boner.

The Base Clutch

Tighten your thumb and forefinger around the base of the shaft, pressing down on the balls. This will cut off the blood (acting as an impromptu cockring) and help you steady the shaft in your hand. If the skin on it is slick and immutable, you can stroke the penis with more friction, thereby augmenting the excruciating experience.

The Love Tug

As you are stroking him, lightly pull on the wispy strands of pubic hair sprouting from his testicles. Don't pull so hard that you remove them, but tease them gently, lovingly. This will make him holler with delight and awe at your inventiveness.

Other variations include:

The Two-Timer

Tickle his balls with one hand while the other jerks him up and down.

A Joint Effort

The Thigh Swatter

Use the hand that is currently unemployed to firmly but lovingly pat his inner thighs.

Best Fist Forward

Place your fist against his perineum as you're stroking him. He'll probably start opening his legs a little wider, giving you more space to press against. Guaranteed to drive him wild.

The Chestnuts

I call a man's nipples "chestnuts" because they are a primary erogenous zone that happens to be located on his chest. Massage one of his nipples while you masturbate him. Spin the little pink and brown areole between your thumb and forefinger as if you were trying to find a good station on the radio. Men's nipples are less tender than a woman's and therefore can sustain much more tugging and pulling. But they are sensitive little devils whose power and influence should not be underestimated. If you've finished hanging the wash, take a clothespin and clip it onto his nipple. That'll get his attention.

The Hair-Trigger

The ultimate touch! The term hair-trigger is usually used in the context of premature ejaculation, but I'm referring to a little trick of using one's hair during mutual masturbation that is a marvelous way of giving your lover an orgasm that is long overdue. While you're moving your hands up and down, rhythmically, lean forward and let your hair cascade over his testicles and the bottom of his shaft. This will send intense quivers of delight throughout his body. One note of caution, don't let him come in your hair—Nellie Forbush might have been able to wash that man right out of her hair, but you might find it more difficult.

The Pièce de Résistance

Slipping on a plastic or latex glove that you lubricate with a dab of vaseline or KY Jelly, lightly massage his anus as you milk him. Usually, this bit of manipulation is the final straw that will snap the humpy camel's back. He will not be able to restrain from coming if you push the tip of your finger inside the anus. His muscles will contract and clutch your finger inside of him. Both of you will be surprised by how intense his orgasm is. If you've gone in far enough to tickle his "Oh-Gee!" Spot, then you've truly become a topnotch mutual masturbator! Good going!

THIRD BASE—FEMALE STIMULATION

There is a wonderful poem in Gertrude Stein's collection of writings called *Tender Buttons* in which she emphatically declares, "Peeled pencil choke. Rub her coke." You'd have to be Miss Stein, I suppose, to really know what she means by that expression, but my impression is that the "peeled pencil choke" refers to fellatio, and the "rub her coke" is all about clitoral stimulation. In fact, I think "coke" is a wonderful euphemism for the clitoris, sounding sort of like cock, but having a succinct, open ring to it.

Clearly, if a couple wants to succeed in bed the man is going to have to know just as much about manual stimulation as the woman. Now that we've gone over the specifics of giving the perfect hand job, let's take a look at the other side, where the grass may not be any greener, but it's certainly more lush.

Cum Digito

That's latin for "with your fingers." The sex organs of the female are innately designed for manual stimulation. Reach down and place your five fingers against her genitals. See how perfectly the hand cups the vulva and mons pubis? The pressure of your hand alone is enough to give intense gratifying pleasure, but don't hesitate to delicately stroke the slender groove between the labial lips. As your middle finger caresses the vaginal orifice, lightly apply pressure with your outer fingers on the labia majora. Move your hand ever so slowly against the entire genital region—gently—lovingly—adoringly.

With your thumb, reach up and tenderly graze the clitoris, bear down on it for a split second, then twirl your thumb around it, fleetingly flicking at it.

Begin to slip your finger inside her vagina. Not so fast. Let her anticipate the motion. Now lightly move the ball of your finger, right up to the first joint. Twirl it, and feel how splendidly moist and warm it is inside.

Feel the flesh envelop the fat of your finger, move the tip back and forth . . . and back again. Dazzle her with your digital dexterity.

Now pressing down on the mons veneris, let your finger dig in deeper, up to the second knuckle. If your fingernail is on the bottomside, bring your finger up and apply light, yet insistent pressure on the anterior wall of the vagina, the supposed home of the G-Spot.

What a garden of earthy delights! Don't forget the clitoris, the labia minora and majora, and the vaginal opening. Caress the perineum. You can even stroke her anus with a finger from your free hand.

One variation of this hand technique is to place your thumb inside her vagina and press down on the clitoris with your four fingers. This way you can massage the mons veneris, too.

Why not white knuckle it? Push your two middle fingers' knuckles up and down the crack of her lips, and stroke the skin along her inner thighs with your pinky and thumb.

Bring both hands down and part the pink sea—see for yourself what all the fuss is about. The delectable delicacies of the vulva. Thrill as she lubricates herself, making every nook and cranny glisten with . . . anticipation!

Why not caress her nipples while you toy with her vagina? Hold her entire body tight against yours as you stroke her furiously to orgasm. Feel her tighten, grimace, contort. Ultimately, she'll collapse in your arms as wave after wave of breathtaking pleasure rocks her body.

Give her a rest. Then catapult her onto a second, third, and fourth orgasm via your loving hand. Why not treat her to a whirring dervish with a go-around with a vibrator?

NON-MANUAL TECHNIQUES

I hope I'm not giving you the impression that mutual masturbation is limited to the use of the hands! Hardly. There are countless ways to bring someone to the brink of sexual bliss. Spring for the ACCU-JAC II and you can have a whale of a time together. Then again, you don't have to resort to mechanical means. I remember the story of an imaginative young lady who was busy with two boys at the same time. She masturbated one with her hands, and the other, who was all the way at the other end of the bed kissing her thighs, she brought to climax with her toes. Perhaps most of you can not perform with the same pedal dexterity, but you can certainly emulate her enthusiasm and ingenuity.

I Get a Kick Out of You

Sit opposite each other on the bed or the floor and tickle each other's genitals with your respective big toes. This digit is sometimes as big and fat as a small penis. Don't waste its potential!

Women have also been known to have found great pleasure in having a man massage her genital region, especially the mons veneris, with his lower extremity by pressing the ball of his foot up against her. She then has the option of holding his foot in her hand and steering him back and forth. The whole time she maintains control.

STATE-OF-THE-ART SEX

The Ball and Jack

Some of you probably know the expression "basket," which refers to the bulge in a man's pants. Well, here's a little trick shared by an athletically inclined woman. Take a basketball (or any large ball) and slowly roll it along the skin surface of your lover's entire body. You can start at the foot and work your way up. Or if you don't want to beat around the bush, just place the inflated number right on his crotch, making sure you don't drop it! Now, slowly roll it up and down the shaft, around the balls. He'll soon be a basket case.

Take It Off, Take It All Off!

Remember that sexy blonde bombshell who coaxed men across America in a Noxzema commercial to "Take it off, take it all off!"? She was using sex appeal to promote shaving. These days a lot of people are using shaving to promote sex appeal.

A number of people I spoke to advocate mutual pubic hair shaving as an erotic stimulus. Personally I've never tried it. But those who recommend it agree that it is a real turn-on to razor each other in the bath or on a bed. Second, a condom doesn't tear the hairs out of your crotch if they've already been shaved off. Third, the ladies don't have to worry about pubic hair showing out the sides of their bathing suits . . . although I know half a dozen guys who spend all their time on beaches eagerly searching for the stray dynamite gal whose pubes are still there!

Finally, there are certain advantages in terms of the act of sex itself. One, shaving sensitizes the genitals by exposing them more; two, it creates an illusion of early adolescence, which some find amazingly erotic; and three, it gives rise to a layer of stubble that apparently enhances the sensations of intercourse.

I once knew a stripper who used to dance at a bar in Manhattan. One night I came to see her, and she greeted me by loudly proclaiming that she had shaved off all her pubic hair. She then promptly showed me the bald truth. When I asked her why she did it she told me she made more in tips. It made her appear younger, and her patrons felt they were getting more for their money.

PRINCIPLE 12

THE DELIGHTS
DOWN UNDER

How to Enjoy Safe Oral Sex

At last count, there were 14,288,400 possible variations for oral gratification. Naturally, because of AIDS, a lot of them have fallen out of favor. I wish I could tell you that all forms of oral sex are safe, but there still isn't enough reliable data available to make such a claim.

CUNNILINGUS

Although plenty of pamphlets have appeared telling you how to engage in safe sex, very little information has been available on safe sex in terms of cunnilingus. What are the risks?

We've already seen how the AIDS virus can be passed along through vaginal secretions. Therefore, precautions should be taken not to get any of these bodily fluids in the mouth. The virus can enter the bloodstream either through a cut or tear in the gums, or through a similar abrasion or sore on the lips or tongue. For women who experience female ejaculation the problem is exacerbated because of the abundance of secretions flowing throughout the genital region. Pains should be taken to avoid this special secretion too since it is capable of carrying the virus.

Your best bet is to concentrate oral attention on the clitoris, which does not secrete any fluids of its own. Since the clitoris does not have a urethra (as the homologous organ, the penis, does), it is pretty safe to say you can lick it without any risk as long as the entire genital area has been washed thoroughly with soap and water. However, it doesn't take much for a woman to start secreting her own natural lubricant. Most of the fluid is retained in the area from the entrance of the vagina to the outlying vaginal folds. And it is hard to distinguish between that portion of the genital region that has been lubricated naturally, and that which is moistened by saliva.

The solution being offered by safer sex aficionados is called THE DENTAL DAM—a flat square latex shield used in oral surgery that, if stretched, also fits tightly around the vulva. At first reading, the dental dam may sound repugnant. But it's erotic character should not be underestimated. Keep in mind that the primary enjoyment in performing cunnilingus for most men is derived from the proximity of the face to the genitals. Cunnilingus is a deeply intimate act. The same amount of intimacy can be achieved in so-called safe cunnilingus.

I asked "Ken," our satyr-like actor, how he felt using a dental dam. "A lot of women," he answered, "think that a guy doesn't like going down on them. I think women are conditioned to think of their sex organs as ugly or dirty. For me, it's the ultimate prize.

I love tasting a woman's private parts, moving my head between her legs, holding on to each thigh as I dig deeper into her with my tongue. Naturally, the idea of putting a latex sheet between me and her pussy was ridiculous. But hell, I'll try anything once. I went to my dentist and asked him to show me one of these things. I'd had fillings, teeth pulled, bridges inserted, but I didn't have any idea what a dental dam was. Well, let me tell you, after the dentist took one out of a little dusty box on the shelf and handed it to me, I was at a loss for words. It was nothing more than a piece of plastic! Like Glad Wrap, only thicker and darker. I told him I had heard they come in handy during sex. I was afraid to mention the word cunnilingus because I had heard about that Freudian phobia called vagina dentatis in which a guy thinks a woman's got teeth in her cunt, and I wondered how a dentist deals with going down on a woman, so I joked that I'd read about it in *The Atlantic* magazine (which I had!). My dentist's hygenist overheard us talking and suggested I order the dental dam by the gross! After taking the thing home and trying it out, I just might take her up on her offer. I was surprised by how much feeling could be generated simply by putting my tongue against this latex sheet. My girlfriend enjoyed it—and I was able to get my nut by having my face locked between her luscious creamy thighs."

The best way to deal with a dental dam is to eroticize it up front. Play with it just as you did with the condom earlier on. See how easily it is to stretch it, making the latex almost invisible as it covers the skin. Be careful that you don't chew it, since you can tear the dental dam as easily as a condom, too.

"George" told me of his experience with one. "This lady I picked up thought I was crazy for insisting on using the dental dam, but we both were laughing so much, I kind of teased her into it. Once I got down there, and started licking away, she didn't say another word. She was lying so still and stiff that I thought maybe something was wrong. Then I realized that she was so turned on by the way my tongue was thrashing about her pussy that she couldn't even breathe. I continued muff-diving for the longest time. I liked it enough to do it again the next time we got together. It's kind of strange, but that's part of the fun!"

FELLATIO

The *Village Voice*, in a cover story called "AIDS AND YOU: A Practical Guide to Staying Alive," stated that "felatio [sic] without ejaculation" is "possibly safe." Others have looked at it differently, as "not so safe" or "less risky." With that in mind, make your own decision. Those of you who want to adhere to the fundamentals of fearless sex will probably think "possibly" just isn't good enough. For others, the risk seems acceptable.

During fellatio, there are many opportunities where semen can enter the mouth. Most obviously, of course, is at the moment of ejaculation. So orgasms during fellatio are to be strictly avoided. Second, if a man has previously ejaculated there is a strong chance that traces of semen can still be found in his urethral tract, as well as on the skin of the penis. Just because you don't see anything doesn't mean there's nothing there. Third, the virus exists in the pre-ejaculatory fluid, and care should be taken not to make oral contact with this. Fourth, if it turns out that there *is* some danger in exchanging saliva, it is certainly not risk-free to lubricate the head and urethra since these areas of the penis are porous and the virus could theoretically be transferred. If, as I did, you are wondering why the exchange of saliva during kissing is not considered a factor in the transmission of AIDS, but in oral sex it is, bear in mind that the mouth has built-in enzymes whose sole purpose is to destroy germs and viruses. The genitals do not have these protectors.

After such stern warnings, you may well ask what options are left for diehard fellators? The answer— loads of opportunities. As long as you avoid any oral contact with the urethra and the fluids emitted by it, you are relatively safe. This is an advantage fellatio has over cunnilingus, since it is easy to see when the penis is free from its own secretions. Keep your mouth along the shaft and testicles and you have plenty of areas to keep yourself orally occupied.

Hot Kisses

"Debbi," a talented cartoonist from Texas, told me how she likes to kneel down between her husband's legs and kiss the area around his balls. "I start at the base of his right inner thigh, and land a kiss every inch or so until I've moved all the way around his crotch. Then I start all over again on the other side of his left thigh." This routine, she swears, drives her husband wild with pleasure. Others have told me how they like to begin oral sex by kissing their lover's nipples, then slowly making their way down to his loins, lightly kissing the head, the shaft, his testicles, the perineum, and the soft tender areas of his thighs. Special attention should be paid to the surface area of the hips, since most men find these very sensitive, but they are rarely attended to.

(Note: As long as we're talking about the variety of erogenous zones that come into play during oral sex, be apprised that analingus, or "rimming," is considered dangerous by doctors and epidemiologists, not especially as a means of transmitting the HIV virus, but certainly as a means of spreading other serious sexually transmitted diseases including amebiasis, giardiasis, and hepatitis. It is not an ingredient of Terrific Sex.)

Hard Licker

The tongue is very versatile. Let it entertain him. Licking, like kissing, is best when you take your time. "Frank," a mechanic, told me how he likes a woman to "slobber" over his testicles. "It makes me nuts," he declares. "I like it best when my lady starts real slow and nice, slipping her tongue all around my balls, licking the sides, then taking them into her mouth, one at a time, maybe both if she can handle it."

In that vein, "Bette," a voluptuous-looking redhead, told me that she was glad for one thing since AIDS came around. She no longer felt obligated to "blow" her husband. She never liked it in the first place since she had poor reflex control in her throat. When pressed, however, she did reveal that she likes the taste and the texture of a penis. Luckily for her, Bette has discovered that she doesn't have to limit herself to that stereotype of oral sex. She now avails herself of the safe techniques without worrying about what someone else is thinking. She's doing what she likes, and loving it. Her boyfriend's the one who's surprised by what a skilled lover she's become.

Blowin' in the Wind

The word *blow* has often been confused with the term "suck." Frankly, I don't know what the origin of the expression "blow job" is, but in terms of Terrific Sex, true blowing is a wonderful way of adding sensuality to safe oral sex. Why not blow on his penis and testicles? The little gusts of hot air will cause him to gasp and whimper as you work your magic down under.

Love at First Bite

Are you one of the "Nibble-ungen"? As you maneuver yourself close to his genitals, lightly nibble on the flesh of his thighs, his stomach, and his scrotum. Be careful you don't get carried away. And whatever you do—don't break the skin. As Amelia wisely relates, "We all have an obligation to tell someone, please don't bite me there. It causes me unbearable pain."

RUBBER SOUL

As previously stated in the earlier section on condoms, there's no reason to be reticent about using a prophylactic during oral sex. [Although I think it was Woody Allen who said the idea of using a condom during fellatio was pretty hard to swallow.]

"Virginia" is a pretty thirty-two-year-old lawyer working on Wall Street. When the guidelines for safe sex were first distributed she was despondent. They listed fellatio as a not-so-safe thing to do. As a self-proclaimed "sexpot," performing fellatio was one of Virginia's favorite activities. Although she wasn't sure she'd been exposed to the virus, she didn't want to take any more chances. She stopped performing oral sex on men. I asked Virginia what it was about fellatio that was so appealing to her. Her answer surprised me. She said the part of giving head that turned her on the most was the feeling of having a penis inside her mouth. She didn't care if her sex partner came or not. She just loved the way a penis felt. Like Linda Lovelace, her clitoris, she joked, was deep in her throat. I told Virginia that there was no reason why she couldn't continue to enjoy this sensation. All she had to do was put a rubber on the penis. She balked at the idea and said it sounded "pathetic," too "desperate," and she "would rather die than ever resort to that."

I asked her to at least give it a try and let me know whether or not it was all the things she said it was.

She came back smiling. "I tried giving my boyfriend a blow job with a rubber on. And to tell you the truth, I enjoyed it a lot. It didn't feel that much different for me. I mean, I still got that feeling of fullness in my mouth and throat. I'm not so sure my boyfriend got the same amount of pleasure, but what the hell, it was his turn to please me."

Too often we're the first to condemn a practice before we've even tried it. Virginia had to be talked into it. She might never have tried it. I applaud the attitude of an experienced fellatrice named "Meg" who viewed "giving head" to a guy wearing a rubber "like sucking on a huge pacifier." She simply can't get enough. Perhaps you won't identify with her childlike fetish, but you can see if it holds true for you.

Flavor of the Week

Tennessee Williams coyly referred to the penis as "hard candy" underscoring the tastier aspects of oral sex. Ice cream is not the only thing that *comes* in thirty-one different flavors. Connoisseurs of lovemaking have always known that adding flavor to a penis is a splendid way to increase one's sexual pleasure by bringing in other senses—the senses of taste, smell, and texture. "Lauren" likes to spread peanut butter on her lover's penis, especially the crunchy kind that sticks to the roof of her mouth. Another voluptuary suggested dipping your boyfriend's penis in a snifter of V.S.O.P. cognac. Be creative. Try other savory concoctions. Adding flavors is an ingenious method of overcoming the bland taste of a condom when used in oral sex. Try mouthwatering delicacies. Every good girl deserves fudge, or butterscotch, applesauce, whipped cream, raspberry jam, Fluffernut, and even that old American standard, ketchup. No MSG, please.

Through a Glass Starkly

Put a sheet of hard plastic, or glass, over the genital area and lick away at what is perceived through the looking glass. Make sure that the glass is sturdy, solid, and won't slip out from under you. People have been known to improvise this type of behavior by kneeling in front of a window and licking the image of their lover's genitals pressed against the glass. In the film *Midnight Express* the character played by Brad Davis masturbated himself while kissing his girlfriend's breasts through wired glass.

As always, it is the psychological impact of what you are doing that makes the sex so satisfying. Let your mind escape into the uncharted wilderness of fantasy. As a sexual pioneer, it is your manifest destiny to explore the outer limits of your sensuality.

PRINCIPLE 13

A MATTER OF INTERCOURSE

The Fearless Fuck

As a society, and in particular as men, we tend to focus too much attention on the act of orgasm rather than on the act of making love.

It has become common knowledge, at least since *The Hite Report*, that women are too often disappointed by their male partners because the guys come too soon, and then have the audacity to think the sex is over. Or they concentrate so much on having coitus that they neglect other areas of stimulation.

Today, in the midst of a health crisis, it is imperative that we change our notions of what constitutes intercourse. The word, itself, provides the clues to our new approach. *The American Heritage Dictionary* defines intercourse as "dealings or communications between persons or groups." The second meaning, of course, is that of sexual intercourse. The word stems from the Latin verb *intercurrere* meaning "to mingle with." It doesn't say anything about having an orgasm. One sexologist always asks the question, "What four-letter word ending in K means intercourse?" The answer he gives is "talk."

For years women have been saying that the part they love most about having sex is the feeling of being physically close to another human being, of having a man hold them in their arms, of feeling a warm body pressing against their own flesh, of breaking boundaries and territorial limits, of becoming one with someone else in an act of physical union, but in an act that is spiritually binding as well. Most men, if free to talk without any peer pressure, will admit to the same.

In terms of Terrific Sex there are many ways one can continue to enjoy all of these feelings and pleasures. The joy of intercourse doesn't have to depend on whether a man ejaculates inside a woman.

You may be wondering why rubbers are necessary during intercourse if the man doesn't ejaculate. Remember that an orgasm is a tricky thing to control. A lot of men lose all control during the sex act and their bodies take over, releasing semen when they least expect it. A rubber is the best way to make sure that this fluid does not enter the vagina in case of such an occurrence.

And as for anal sex, now is *not* the time to begin exploring this area of heterosexual intercourse. While safe anal sex is possible with the careful use of prophylactics, and gay men have successfully used them, a straight couple engaging in Terrific Sex would be better off avoiding it. As always, K.I.S.S.—Keeping It Sexy, but Simple—is the best tool in removing unnecessary complications.

How then can we enjoy "the fearless fuck"?

Let me *proposition* you.

PROPOSITION I

Take your time.

Let's say the two of you enter into an agreement to engage in safe sexual intercourse. After extended kissing, petting, risk-free oral sex, body massage, and general heavy breathing you're ready to take the plunge. Now ask yourself (and here I'm speaking directly to the male) what is the point of intercourse? To get yourself off? To get both of you off? To be even more physically intimate than you were moments before? To show the full extent of your love?

Fine. Any of these answers is reasonable and sound. Now, think. Do you want it to be over in less than three minutes? Probably not. Then take your mind off reaching a climax. Don't think in terms of how you can work yourself up to an orgasm. I see no reason why you can't continue to give her all the orgasms she wants since her orgasms don't cause her to lose an erection, or reach for a cigarette. But putting the orgasm on the shelf for a while allows *you* so much more freedom—freedom to explore new sensations, to try out different positions, to practice slow and methodical penetration. What better way to devote yourself completely to making sure your partner has a good time too.

PROPOSITION 2

Why not postpone intercourse until after your first orgasm?

This way you don't have to worry about coming too soon, coming too late, not coming at all, whether the rubber is going to break, etc. Let's say you've both reached orgasm by manual means. You're both still excited and want to continue having sex. You're in the mood for a little old-fashioned nooky. Put on a condom. Now you can screw all you want, with the luxury of time, greater pleasure (since the penis is extra sensitive after an initial orgasm), and your partner can continue to share in the experience. If you feel a second orgasm coming on, follow the guidelines of Terrific Sex, and ejaculate outside the body.

PROPOSITION 3

Try different, more provocative sex positions!

If you're engaged in intercourse in the famous Missionary Position and you feel an orgasm coming on, slow down, tell your partner that you wish to change positions. The slight respite will help you to back off from coming, and the new position usually takes a minute or two to get used to.

What are some other valuable positions?

Come from Behind

There's the perennial favorite—REAR ENTRY (inter-course *a tergo,* or *a posteriori*) in which a woman chooses to be penetrated from behind. In such cases, the woman can be kneeling, facing forward, standing, or bending over. She could also be lying on her stom-ach, legs spread, or held aloft in the man's arms. Many men prefer the rear angle of insertion because it feels more natural. The curve of the penis fits the shape of the vagina differently from this angle, affording greater friction. Women also like it because clitoral stimulation is much easier. The man or the woman, or both, can massage the clitoris freely.

It has been suggested in many studies that REAR ENTRY provides greater excitation of the female geni-talia, in particular the G-Spot located on the ventral wall of the vagina. Indeed, it is certainly worth con-sidering why mankind is the only mammal that doesn't always practice this position of intercourse as a matter of rule. Grafenberg himself posited the view in 1953 that "the location of the erogenic zone on the an-terior wall of the vagina proves that the human animal is built in the same manner as the other quadrupeds." He goes on to say "therefore the normal position would be intercourse *a posteriori.*"

You're the Top

Another position that has recently been more in vogue is the WOMAN ON TOP scenario. Here the woman climbs aboard the man's erection and fucks *him.* She has four choices: a) facing forward; b) facing away; c) facing left; or d) facing right. If she's truly industrious (and stouthearted) she can try the SPINNING JENNY, an exercise in which she constantly switches positions, swinging all the way around.

The Woman on Top scenario has the added benefit of allowing the woman much more control. She can rock back and forth on top of the man's crotch, thereby stimulating her clitoris, as well as her perineum and anus. Plus, the Woman on Top scenario affords the man the pleasure of deeper penetration and more freedom to relax, to feel the sensations surrounding his penis. Also, he doesn't have to worry about propping himself up. This is a position that large, heavyset men go for, but I suggest you all give it a shot.

The SITTING PRETTY scenario is an offshoot of the Woman On Top method. Here the female (keeping the penis inside her) slides down and plants herself facing the male, with both their buttocks positioned on the floor. His penis still in her, they lock hands, and rock back and forth.

Taking Sides

The SIDE POSITION is great for kissing and hugging while making love. Lay side by side facing each other. Both of your rear ends are exposed and you can get your hands around them, squeezing them and carressing them. This method is also nice because you can easily switch around and start performing safe oral sex, à la soixante-neuf.

The SPOON RIVER is a variant of the Side Position in which the participants do not face each other. The merits of this position include greater proximity and flexibility, freedom to hug, added warmth, and greater hip movement in the male. Also, this position grants the man greater ability to stimulate the woman's clitoris.

Cream Puff

There's a popular expression, "The bigger the cushion, the better the pushin.'" It refers to the questionable theory that fat women make better lovers because their vaginas are propped up by their Rubensesque buttocks. In such situations, a pillow will suffice. Place a tiny cushion underneath your partner's buttocks in such a way that the hips are raised and the vagina is positioned at an angle that allows you to enter efficiently and with greater ease.

Hard Core

More acrobatic lovers might like to try methods of intercourse that require greater strength and stamina. Many times, the sheer exertion involved in achieving these positions is more stimulating than the act itself.

The LIFT OFF is such a position. Here the man lifts the woman up in his arms. She's facing him, her legs outstretched or wrapped around his hips. She can therefore press down fully on his erection. Together they rock back and forth, until they come or get too tired and collapse on all fours.

Nor is it to be discouraged to experiment with exercise equipment. I once read of a woman who liked to lift herself up with an exercise bar that she attached in her doorway. This way her husband could perform oral sex on her while standing, and she could also hang upside down and do him. When screwing, she was able to swing back and forth. Obviously this woman had admirable talents, but I don't believe such traits are necessarily rare.

The PUSH UP. In this the man makes love with the woman while holding himself aloft in a push up

163

position. Exhausting, maybe, but at times, utterly necessary.

PROPOSITION 4

The man can choose what type of orgasm he wants.

When and if you decide that you do want to come, look at your options. You can come while fucking, so long as you have a rubber on, but it is very important to remember that condoms are not foolproof and they sometimes break. Your safer bet is to withdraw before orgasm and come outside the vagina. The "Out of Body, Out of Mind" catchphrase works very well here. Once out of the vagina, you can either leave the rubber on, or take it off, whichever makes you more comfortable.

Why not postpone your orgasm until after the woman has reached climax, and continue the sexual play, but in a different, safer format? This way, when you come, you won't be putting anyone at risk.

Very often, our concentration on orgasm can lead to a number of disturbing side effects. Here are some problems that arise. Come what may, they can be resolved.

The "O-No!"

Otherwise known as *ejaculatio praecox*, premature ejaculation is a common problem among men. Kinsey reported that seventy-five percent of all American men ejaculated within two minutes of penetration, usually after a total of some forty to fifty thrusts. He considered this response a "superior mammalian trait." Nevertheless, next to anxiety over penis length, premature ejaculation is the most significant sexual dysfunction afflicting the American male.

Premature ejaculation occurs most frequently among men who could be labeled "hypertonic"—a person who suffers from nervous exhaustion, insomnia, fatigue, and digestive and circulatory disorders. For instance, if a man works all day under a great deal of stress, at the New York Stock Exchange, or at a high-paced factory, his nervous system might be reduced to a complex system of fits and jerks.

The best way to handle this situation is to see a doctor or a sex therapist as soon as possible. Don't let this problem get worse by not confronting it. One method of taking the pressure off your lover is what has become known as "sensate focus" treatment. It is a means of giving pleasure without introducing the idea of sexual performance. Get your partner to lie back, positioning his body so that his back is pressed against a bedboard or a large firm pillow. You sit in front, facing him, his legs spread, allowing you free access to his genitals. Gently suggest to him that he try and think of the pleasure he's giving you by letting you touch him. This will relieve his sense of performance anxiety, a common cause of premature ejaculation and impotence. Don't expect any miracles immediately. It takes time to develop trust and sexual intimacy. Usually, if both partners are caring and thoughtful, the problem can be resolved.

The "Uh-O!"

Premature ejaculation pales as a problem in comparison to impotence. "Malcolm" is a highly successful writer of bestselling romances. He has an enormous reading public of devoted fans. He can write knowingly about love, passion, and sex—but in bed he has a severe case of writer's block. He's impotent.

He's tried everything to overcome this problem: hypnosis, electrotherapy, cock rings, and splints. He's used drugs, aphrodisiacs, ointments, as well as suppositories that are supposed to give him a lift. He's tried injections. He even contemplated having a prosthetic device implanted into his penis. That would mean having a permanent erection (albeit, via scientific priapism) but at least his cock would be hard.

It was not until he started meeting regularly with a sex surrogate that he discovered any relief. It was learned that his problem was not solvable through medicine or voodoo sex gadgets; his dysfunction was psychological. The "post office" test had proved it. Under the direction of his sex therapist, Malcolm wrapped several connected postage stamps around his cock at night. In the morning the perforations were torn, proving flat out that he was physically capable of having an erection. Most men have two or three erections at night during sleep.

Eventually, Malcolm was able to get over his dysfunction because he recognized the problem and was willing to discuss it. Unfortunately in most cases, help is not sought. Men hope to surmount their difficulties by some sort of triumph of the will. If his problem is psychologically based, no amount of willpower is going to resolve his difficulties. Understanding, patience, and practice will prove much wiser remedies.

The Double-O

Here is one anomaly that, while uncommon, is hardly a cause for concern. Most men don't think they are capable of multiple orgasms. But almost everyone can have a Double-O. This type of orgasm occurs during sex when a man refrains from pausing between orgasms and continues to stimulate himself as if he hasn't climaxed. This does not mean he has to ignore the immense pleasures of the first orgasm, but he must not collapse, breath a heavy sigh, roll over, or hop in the bathroom for a quick shower.

Please note that if this occurs during intercourse, and the man is using a rubber, it is best to take "the pause that refreshes" and change rubbers.

But if the orgasm is taking place outside of the body, as recommended in the Terrific Sex guidelines, then there is no reason why he can't continue on to a second orgasm. To dramatize how the Double-O works, let me recount John's story.

"I was having sex with my girlfriend, Lori, and we were rolling around on the bed, fully clothed. She was lying on her stomach and I was dry-humping her behind. I was so excited that I came after only a few minutes, but I didn't want the sex to stop. Nor did she. I didn't change positions, and so continued to pump away, rubbing my cock against her soft buttocks. Meanwhile my hands were doing a number on her tits. She was moving her hips back and forth and I could see that she was stroking herself wildly down there. Pretty soon she was crying out that she was coming, and I found myself coming too. I couldn't believe it. I'd a second orgasm in just a few minutes!"

One of the reasons that double orgasms don't happen more often for men in the context of a single sexual session is that they are trained to think of an ejaculation as the culmination and conclusion of a sex act. It may be a climax, but it certainly is not the end of the story. Nor should you wind down into a denouement. We place too much importance on the climax, and not enough on the sensations leading up to orgasm.

The Mega-O

Most men have discovered while masturbating that they can control when and how they come by learning the telltale signs of an approaching climax. The stimulation of the penis and the surrounding erogenous zones creates a threshold of pleasure that once crossed can no longer be contained. An ejaculation is imminent, and the desire for one, preeminent. If the ejaculation is delayed, an interesting thing takes place. An "unfolding" of pleasure spreads throughout the genital area, creating a warm, satisfying feeling that increases in intensity the more it occurs. By avoiding the emission of semen, a man can continue to enjoy numerous orgasmic experiences that are not dependent upon an ejaculation. This is the secret zone of pleasure that is too often denied. A true sex connoisseur can develop and train and time his climaxes so that they last longer, feel stronger, and satisfy more.

A man can learn and train himself not to exceed this threshold. Just as he comes close to ejaculating he can hold back. How? a) by slowing down; b) by removing stimulation (taking a hand off, withdrawing, separation, etc.); c) by wearing a cock ring; d) by clasping the base of the shaft and squeezing tight; e) by dramatically changing his focus of attention, ie. thinking of other subjects (like bills that have to be paid, non-exciting subjects like math or engineering, etc.); f) by talking matter-of-factly with his partner.

Once you've mastered this technique there is no reason why you can't enjoy the Mega O at all times, whether you're mutually masturbating, engaging in intercourse, having oral sex, or indulging in auto-eroticism.

The Invisible O

Did you know that sexologists are researching whether there are actually two types of male orgasm? The phallic—and the anal? Women have debated the verity of clitoral versus vaginal orgasms, and now men have taken sides regarding the existence of a prostatic orgasm that may be accompanied by an ejaculation of prostatic fluid. In *The Hite Report On Male Sexuality*, devotees of prostatic manipulation claim that they can experience different orgasmic sensations if their prostate gland is stroked sufficiently. One man expressed his experience with his wife. "Once she put me across her lap, put her finger up my ass, and felt around until she found my prostate . . . She started kneading it with her finger . . . It took a while and finally I came. I never really got an erection and there wasn't much fluid either. But it was great." The feeling has been depicted as "more internal and all around the pelvic region."

Even better—a man can enhance his phallic orgasm by complementing it with an ecstatic prostatic one. During intercourse a woman can insert her finger up her lover's rectum and rub him the right way. Or she can insert a vibrator or long, easily grasped object into him.

PROPOSITION 5

Why not experiment with methods of non-vaginal, non-anal, non-oral intercourse?

What, you might ask, could these be? Well, the Greeks were great at figuring out ways to have sex that did not entail insertion of the penis inside the body. There were a number of diseases going around in those days, too, probably more, and contraception was almost non-existent. People were wise to come up with various substitutes for coitus.

The Tenderloin District

The THIGHS provide an excellent alternative. Scholars of ancient Greek history politely call "thighfucking" interfemoral intercourse. Depictions of it abound on the many Greek vases in museums and private collections. What interfemoral means is that the guy slides his penis between his partner's thighs directly below the groin. Here the flesh is soft, warm and with the right amount of lubricant, deliciously moist. If you don't think this is a satisfying alternative, listen to an account by "Rick" of his first lesson in interfemoral sex. It was anything but ephemeral.

"I was really eager to make it with my girlfriend at the time but she was afraid to. She wanted to wait. I thought she was crazy. This was long before AIDS. So I kept asking her, and finally in the throes of hot and heavy making out, I asked her again and she said yes.

170

I couldn't believe it. She offered to direct me inside of her and I felt her hand take my cock and slide it inside her pussy. It was real tight, and it felt incredible. I started pounding away and pretty soon I came. Then when I moved to pull out I realized that she had conned me. I wasn't even inside her. I had been fucking her between her thighs."

Not to be outdone, a woman can respond by straddling her boyfriend's thigh and fuck his muscular limb by moving her vulva back and forth in quick, determined thrusts. The thigh is large enough that a woman can clutch it between her legs, and maintain a firm bulkhead on which to eagerly squirm.

One other variation is the BATTERING RAM, where the man presses his bent knee up against a woman's vagina and fucks her without penetration. Although the clitoris gets quite a workout, a shattering climax is soon forthcoming.

The PALM SUNDAE is another ingenious stroke. Here the woman grasps the man's penis in her fist which she positions firmly between her thighs. This way when he's fucking her, the tip of his cock keeps getting milked by her fist and the sensations are remarkably acute.

The Golden Calf

Technically known as "intercrural intercourse," this position involves piercing the space created by the union of the two calves. With the proper lotion, and motion, enough friction can be built up to bring on a blistering orgasm. This is another example where excess body fat is a welcome blessing.

Bottoms Up!

The buttocks have always been a beacon for lovers of exotic sex. Here the gentleman mounts his partner from behind, thrusting his penis between her buttocks. Slowly rubbing his shaft back and forth along the erogenous zone of her crack, he can fuck like mad without any risk. Meanwhile he can fondle her vagina and clitoris as he pounds away on top of her. The extra-special effect of this position is that the man can also press his testicles against the firm flesh of her buttocks while he's fucking. This bonus is not usually possible in vaginal or anal intercourse, and is therefore an unbeatable side effect that should not be missed.

Bosom Buddies

One of the most popular forms of non-genital contact is breast fucking. Here the woman presses her breasts around her lover's penis and massages him to orgasm. Depending on the size and shape of her breasts, tit fucking can be performed in deep thrusts or light touches of the penis against her warm skin. Men and women adore this position because either one can control the pressure of the breasts against the penis. For women whose breasts are not very large, the man can simply rub his corona back and forth across one of her nipples.

Versatility is a real plus in this position. The man can shift positions, moving and leaning forward, bringing his testicles towards the woman's face, letting her flick her tongue across his testicles. He then has the option of sliding back and forth between these complementary erogenous zones.

PROPOSITION 6

Don't forget that the best part of intercourse is what happens after. The Final Touch.

Surveys have shown that a lot of people engage in sex just so they can enjoy those comforting postpartum moments of hugging, lying together, and spooning that come after coitus.

After the lengths each of you has gone during the act of intercourse, breaking down all barriers between you, this period of repose and reflection is a perfect time to just relax and allow the sensations of being with the one you love wash over you. For some, it's the fact that they're not alone, that there is a living, breathing, physical being next to them who, by his or her mere presence, reassures, protects, and nourishes the spirit. As one young man sees it, "after you've made love, you wonder what is there left to hide? You feel less restricted. It's the intimate discussion afterwards that makes sex so special."

Post-sex is a period for tenderness, for laughter, and quite often tears. Let them flow. Your nervous system has undergone a tremendous workout. The freedom of expression and flood of emotions that follows is totally normal, expected and deserved.

Don't forsake these exquisite moments of intimacy by suddenly jumping up and running to the bathroom to rinse away what you perceive as your guilty, sick feelings. There is such a thing as post-coital depression, but it is merely a momentary lull in one's elation that I assume is Mother Nature's clever way of making sure a clasping, lovemaking couple finally separate. Don't overreact to this quick, temporary depression. Pass through it. Within seconds, you'll feel even more close, affectionate, and trusting with your partner.

It's best not to overstimulate the genitals or nipples. They're still in overload and need a recess. Touching, caressing, and massage work better après sex. Kissing, of course, is the supreme gesture of love. If you don't kiss after sex, it might imply to your partner that you've lost interest, that you're not satisfied, or that you somehow feel ashamed. You don't have to resort to heavy necking to make your point, but do make sure you at least bend over, plant a friendly kiss, and say thanks.

PART THREE

THE FANTASTIC SIDE
OF TERRIFIC SEX

PRINCIPLE 14

THE ROMANCE OF SEX

What makes sex so erotic?

Ninety-nine percent of the time, it's psychological. It's not how it feels that makes sex so fantastic, it's what it *means*.

In this section, we'll cover those areas in which we can improve the meaning of sex, by imbuing it with romance and adventure.

ATMOSPHERE

Diana Vreeland has called atmosphere "the great seducer." A room can invoke sensuality as easily as a sexy picture or an illustration can. Think of your apartment as a stage set with the utmost care to create a powerful dramatic effect. Load it with atmosphere. Put a scented red scarf over a lamp. Set up candles all

177

around the room. Place a variety of plump, curvaceous cushions on your couch or bed. Get a sheepskin rug to roll around on.

Pick some music that will add an undertone of raw animal magnetism. The "Bolero" is famous, but have you ever considered Tchaikovsky's "Pathétique" for mood music? The music of Scriabin is sure to get the juices flowing. Or maybe you prefer the evocative, sensuous dance music of the Cariocas—the sambas and merengues. The bossa nova or the captivating dance of the Argentine, the tango. An old LP of ol' blue eyes, Frank Sinatra, or Margaret Whiting singing "Moonlight In Vermont" could warm the heart of the coldest of dates.

Do you pay much attention to the clothes you're wearing before sex? Before you utter those immortal words, "Let me slip into something more comfortable," ask yourself the revealing question, "Would I rather look comfortable or sexy?" Comfortable for a lot of us means dirty jeans, ragged sweatshirts, and old slippers. That could be a turn-off.

Figure out how you want to look before dressing. Try and second-guess what your partner is into. Does he or she like gymnastics, aerobics, or sports? Then don a pair of running shorts. Or slip on a pair of colorful sweatpants. These new spandex pants have revolutionized the sports industry but they've also galvanized voyeurs and exhibitionists across the globe. Nothing fits like a pair of spandex pants, and if you've got the body, then flaunt it. Feeling the soft curves of a woman's body through this incredibly textured material is an absolute turn-on. The look and feel of a man who wears one of these items is an equally stimulating experience. Not to mention the priceless thrill one experiences simply wearing them oneself. The pressure the taut fibers exert on the skin is palpably erotic. A must for serious connoisseurs of romantic seduction.

Greet your date in dance tights. Or simply open the door in your panty hose. The sight of your nakedness underneath the sheer fabric will delight even the most jaded voyeur. Men are only beginning to understand the immense effect they have running around in their skivvies. Try wearing a jockstrap more often. Or a bathrobe with nothing else on.

Another potent mood-changer is a baggy pair of overalls. "Candice," a dance instructor from Maryland, confided how she likes to make love with her husband after he's been tinkering with the car. "My husband works all week at a nine-to-five office job. He's always wearing a tie and a jacket. But on weekends, he often puts on a pair of overalls to work around the yard or on the car. Sometimes I do a double take because I can't believe that's my husband out there with grease on his face and hands, carrying a wrench. One afternoon, it was boiling hot and humid. He had the radio blaring in the station wagon while he was washing it. The sweat was pouring off him. I happened to walk by and the thought struck me that if he was so hot maybe I should spray him with the hose. At first he wasn't laughing, but after a while he warmed up and grabbed me, kissing me. I could taste the salty sweat on his lips and feel the heat of him seep through his overalls. I reached down and felt him inside the thick denim. I was getting all wet inside. I whispered in his ear that he could finish washing the car later. Upstairs we had some of the best sex we've ever had."

If the weather is colder, why not jump into a pair of snow pants? Or just walk around in your ski boots. (Watch out for those ski poles!) Be creative. Infuse the air around you with an attitude of spontaneity and healthy sexual inventiveness.

Don't forget that what you dress in is also what

you'll be taking off later. It's hard to perform a sensuous striptease if you're wearing eight layers of clothes. Your partner will fall asleep before it's over.

Likewise, don't wear pads (for shoulders, or falsies, or, if you're a guy, a little something extra in the crotch). These can fall out at the most inopportune moments.

PLACES OF THE HEART

What could be duller than making love in the same bed day in, day out? Use your imagination. Roll out the sleeping bag that's packed in the back of your closet. Take out your summer lounge furniture and set it up in the living room. Do it on the couch, on the rug, on the cool tiled floor of your bathroom! Give it a shot in the basement, or on top of the dryer in the laundry room. The whirring of the machine can only add to your enjoyment. If all else fails, hop into the backseat of your car while it's in the garage and go at it there. Pretend you're parking on lover's lane. Or better yet, hightail it up there as soon as possible.

"Marc," a writer, related his conversion to eccentric lovemaking environments. During a trip to Washington, D.C., where he was staying with a former college roommate, he met an attractive woman who lived a few houses away with her family. She didn't want them to know she was home, so she invited Marc into her steamy indoor swimming pool. After skinny-dipping, they ended up on the diving board. Marc located a tube of Coppertone on a table nearby and asked Susy to give him a rubdown. Eventually they kissed, petted, and ultimately masturbated each other to orgasm, using the tanning lotion as a lubricant. Marc says it was one of the most exciting sexual experiences he's ever had. And it was entirely because of the atmosphere—plus the fact they surrendered to their creative imaginations.

The possibilities for ingenious atmospheres are endless. "Melanie" was shopping with her boyfriend at a local department store in Philadelphia. They took the wrong elevator and ended up downstairs at the loading dock. Before she could say a word, her boyfriend kissed her and proceeded to rub his body tight against hers, grabbing her breasts and pressing his hard cock against the soft, tender puff of her mons veneris. The sound of trucks backing into the garage, the smell of gasoline and grease, the roar of the generators and the oppressive hum of the elevator shaft behind her, caused her to get lost in a sexual reverie. Although they didn't have sex, per se, they definitely had a sexual experience. Thanks again, to atmosphere.

Indulge your fantasy, don't be afraid to explore new terrains, or propel yourself to new heights of awareness. The world is a fabulous cornucopia of refreshing, exotic, sensational environments for sensual lovemaking. Choose wisely, partake gladly!

PRINCIPLE 15

MIND BLOWERS

The Fantasy
of Sex

We all have sexual fantasies. The curious thing is most of us don't think they're sexual.

When we think about sexual fantasies we tend to think of more extreme types of behavior, bizarre scenarios—the rape of the Sabine women, Lord Byron ripping off our bodice, General Burnside burrowing beneath our bloomers, Amelia Earhart in black leather panties spanking us with a propeller. But just thinking about how nice it would be to have sex with someone is a sexual fantasy.

Every time we look at a sex symbol at the movies, or in a magazine, and we imagine what he or she must look like naked, or how their skin must feel, or even what their lips might taste like if they were pressing against our own, we are indulging in sexual fantasizing. As Nancy Friday has said, "a fantasy is a map of desire." It delineates what our special areas of sexual arousal are. Many of these are extraordinary forms of sexual behavior: S&M, rape, abduction, bondage and humiliation, orgies, troilism (threesomes), watersports, voyeurism, exhibitionism, and fetishes, etc.

Mind Blowers

During adolescence most of us were acutely aware of our sexual daydreaming, because these sensuous reveries had an obvious impact on us. Guys would get "boners," and girls would get all "hot and bothered." We would lose ourselves in hours of erotic daydreaming. As we matured we learned how to control our bodies, to focus our libidinous energies into more direct outlets—dating, creative pursuits, and for some of us, spirituality. As a result, we learned how to deny our fantasies.

A study published in *The Journal of Sex Research* in 1986 (and cited in *The New York Times* by Jane Brody) revealed that eighty-eight percent of the women interviewed reported having fantasies, and one fourth of them claimed to have them regularly. The study surmised that "sexual fantasies . . . represent a very personal experience to be enjoyed rather than viewed as detrimental to their overall sexual adjustment."

Are you afraid that your sexual wishes might come true? This is a common fear and one that has been shown to be completely unfounded. The vast majority of people leave their sexual fantasies in the realm of the imagination and rarely if ever venture out to experiment with them in actuality. Just because you think of something doesn't make it true.

For instance, if you have a rape fantasy, it doesn't follow that you want to be raped. A fantasy is not a dream. It does not reveal latent content—nor can it be interpreted to the same degree. We live in a society where our minds and imaginations are bombarded at every turn by seductive, intensely provocative images. Sometimes these ideas or pictures trigger fantasies in our head. There is no reason why we should avoid mentally exploring these notions, thereby allowing ourselves the chance to discover more of what moves us, entices us, beckons us.

"Helen," a married woman who works as an interpreter at the U.N., decried the fact that she was "too normal." She didn't "have any fantasies at all!" Her problem (and I use the word problem because her attitude was one of displeasure, not pride) stems from the fact that she refused to perceive her thoughts as sexual. Later, she was able to confess to me that she loves to think about men kissing her back. Just the idea of it sends tingles up and down her spine. I suggested to her that this could be construed as a sexual fantasy—quite a strong one since merely thinking of it created a potent physical sensation. This talented linguist learned that at any given moment, when she needs to call on a device that will enable her to relax sexually, or to experience sensual stimulation, she can call on this fantasy. So can you.

A lot of people think it is wrong to think about another person or other people while in bed with someone they're romantically interested in. There might be some reason for concern if the *only* way you are able to respond to the person you are with is by invoking images of someone else. But during the course of lovemaking, it is perfectly natural to be reminded of past sexual experiences, or a running fantasy of a particular person or image which turns you on. Or you might fantasize about a completely fictional character, Superman, King Kong, Mata Hari, The Sixty Foot Woman. Don't become guilty and freeze up. Relax and let the parade of faces, body parts, and feelings pass by. This is really one of the most enjoyable parts of sex—letting go and allowing your subconscious free rein.

What if you want to act on a shocking, but harmless fantasy? Let's say you have always dreamed of seeing your girlfriend attired in a sexual costume relating to a personal fetish you have. Talk about it.

Bring up the subject the next time it's appropriate—and feasible. You might want to save the experience until it's practical. For instance, if you are dying to make love to your wife while she is dressed as a nun, the night of a costume party is probably the best time to make your dream come true.

I am reminded of the story of a college student who fantasized about one day making it with Dolly Parton. On Halloween he met a girl at a mixer who was dressed as Miss Parton, outfitted with two big balloons stuffed inside her sweater. That night, the guy was able to fulfill a lifelong fantasy by seducing the Dolly double. Although I did not speak to the girl, I imagine that she was fulfilling her own fantasy of being made love to as if she were a blonde bombshell. Don't forget that in sex, both of you are fantasizing. Hopefully, the two fantasies can complement each other—and neither of you has to burst each other's balloons.

How do you become better acquainted with your own libidinous fantasies? Once again, go back to your Sex Bio. Not only will you uncover past experiences that will become the source and feeding ground for your sexual fantasies, but you'll discover those attitudes and concepts that have been ingrained in you since you were a child. It has often been speculated that our deepest and most satisfactory sexual fantasies are those that are based on our earliest sexual experiences. The first time we experienced lust, or genital excitation, or fell in love we were feeling it as an overpowering, alien, mystifying sensation, a feeling that we will probably never forget (unless the experience was negative and we tend to repress it, thus causing serious sexual problems, which is why doing the Sex Bio is so crucial).

"Chrissy" recounts that her first sexual experience

took place in college with a female teacher's assistant. Now that she's married and has three kids and runs a restaurant, she often finds herself drifting off into erotic daydreams, recalling the times she made it with her teacher. In bed, with her husband, she likes it best when he takes control, instructing her in lovemaking, because it reminds her of her first woman lover. Chrissy doesn't feel it necessary to tell her husband that she sometimes has lesbian fantasies. For now, it's a private matter. She's using fantasy constructively.

"Brian" is a piano player and songwriter. He once worked as a shoe salesman in his hometown of Midland, Texas. One time he noticed that a woman whose foot he was fitting with a shoe wasn't wearing any underwear under her skirt. The position he was in, his youth, and his subservient role have all added up to a remarkable fantasy. Now when he is in bed with a woman, Brian likes her to keep her shoes on, even when she's completely naked. This way he can indulge his footwear fetish while fantasizing about his earlier close encounter.

Do you recognize any similar incidents in your past?

Another way of creating a sexual fantasy is to open your mind to new experiences. If you have narrowed yourself down to being a person who only likes a certain type—e.g., tall, blonde, blue-eyed or short, dark, and Oriental—you are cutting yourself off from a world of other possibilities. You are probably denying something in yourself.

In the end, remember that sex and relationships don't have to be neat or easily defined to be healthy. This is not the type of safe sex I'm advocating. In sexual affairs, as in life, you have to take certain risks to develop and grow, to unlock your subconscious, to feel yourself striving toward your full erotic potential.

EROTICA

Erotica, too, can be a healthy stimulus for sexual fantasizing. Some people I spoke with were worried that pornography might be a threat to a couple's relations. Clearly, the answer depends on how the pornography is being used. If a man comes home from work, ignores his wife, and masturbates by himself to a *Penthouse* magazine in the bathroom, there is something wrong with the relationship. The pornography is merely a symptom of a greater problem, obviously not the cause. But if this same man were to share the magazine with his wife, letting her in on his secret, it might indeed enhance their relationship. As one woman sees it, "I might find it distasteful, but it isn't threatening."

"Maria" found some of her husband's pornography in a suitcase in the back of a closet. Rather than throw it out and yell at him when he came home, she asked him about it and when he started to hem and haw she said that looking at it had stimulated her sexually. That night as they undressed on the bed, she flipped through the magazine with him and they both got so excited that they made love without even undoing the covers. Now they watch erotic videos together occasionally and have found a new dynamic that greatly increases their sexual habits. She is fascinated by the way her husband responds to the films. "Watching him react to the naked women turns me on," she says. "I don't know why. Maybe it's discovering new things that he thinks are sexy."

"Paula" didn't respond as warmly to the notion of her husband owning pornography. She told him it was sick and that if he continued to look at it, he'd become addicted and would soon lose interest in her. What she failed to see was that he'd *already* lost interest in her. The pornography was his marital aid. In such drastic cases it doesn't seem like such a bad alternative for a couple to *use* porno as a means of achieving sexual arousal when their own relationship seems to have hit a dry spell. Isn't it better that they're having sex, rather than both pretending that it's not important?

Some people have no reaction to pornography. "Greta" grew up in Romania "where porno didn't exist. When I came to the West, I was curious. In Amsterdam, I went to a couple of live shows and got it out of my system completely. Since then I've had no interest in it. I saw *Emanuelle* but I didn't see *Emanuelle II* or *III*."

"Thomas," an art director for a well-known gay magazine, on the other hand, lives for pornography. "I have pictures of naked men plastered all over my walls. They make me feel good when I wake up in the morning. Unlike some people, I think the human body is beautiful—and should be seen. Some of these photo spreads are as aesthetically pleasing to me as any of the master artworks in the world's great museums." Thomas hopes one day to exhibit his collection.

"Frank," an illustrator, hasn't been able to enjoy pornography since the AIDS crisis began. "For me watching porno flicks is depressing. The performers are encouraged to engage in wildly promiscuous, sometimes dangerous sex—including rimming, cum-drinking, cunt-licking, you name it, they'll do it. I can't help but feel that these days watching a fuck film is like watching a snuff movie." Hopefully, in the future, directors and producers, as well as the performers, will be more conscientious of this problem. In fact, Catalina Video, a popular porno house, has recently sent out ten thousand free safe sex videos to its customers.

Another example of the role pornography can play in increasing sexual compatibility between lovers is a little more complicated. "Belinda" found a cache of S&M magazines in her husband's filing cabinet. She was stunned. If her husband was so into S&M, then maybe she should be concerned. Why hadn't she known? The subject had never come up in the bedroom. Was there something wrong with her that it didn't interest her at all? How could he be two people at the same time? For a moment, Belinda thought her marriage was at risk—and that her sex life would never be the same. Luckily, she took the healthy step of talking to him about it. He admitted he had strong masochistic fantasies, but considered himself normal. He had never brought it up before because he thought she'd be intimidated and embarrassed. The couple remained married because Jack was able to deal with his masochistic urges by masturbating with his pornography when he wanted to. Feeling less guilty, he found that he enjoyed sex with Belinda more, too.

As for married or single women, why not try watching some porno videos yourself when you're alone. There are even some now that are created by women for women, lacking many of the pejorative connotations of some types of mainstream pornography.

AN EROTIC SCRAPBOOK

Is there an ad in a magazine that really gets your juices flowing? Are you in love with a movie star? The "Sexiest Man Alive" who appears in *People* magazine? Do you still have the lock of hair your first steady gave you over twenty years ago? Are all of your past loves documented in a series of Polaroid pictures? Have you kept every back issue of *Playboy* or *Penthouse* (or *Playgirl*) and are running out of room? Why not cut out these pictures, paste them, glue them, staple them, apply them to a scrapbook. Any type of tome will do. A photo album, a diary, even an accordion file. Such a compendium could include not only photographs and pictures but reproductions of paintings, letters, clippings, anything that propels you into a sexually romantic state of mind.

"Roberta" is a songwriter who lives on Manhattan's Upper West Side. She collects "hot shots" of her favorite movie studs, like Richard Gere, Mel Gibson, and Bruce Springsteen, and then makes a collage out of the images. "I find them all over the place. *People* magazine supplies some of the hottest ones. I remember finding a picture of Miles O'Keefe in there that really blew my mind. What a body! What I do when I masturbate is I look at every picture at once, letting my eyes swirl over the page. I project myself into fanciful sexual situations—like I'm backstage at a Bruce Springsteen concert watching him take off his faded blue jeans which are sopping wet with sweat. I offer to help him and one thing leads to another."

I'LL SHOW YOU MINE, IF . . .

Voyeurism and exhibitionism add a great deal to sexual fantasy. "I don't know what came over me," "Evelyn" said. "My husband was in the living room, watching a basketball game. I was bored stiff. So I went upstairs to our bedroom, took off all my clothes and then came back down to him. It took him a minute or so before he noticed that I was standing there stark naked. Of course, he lost interest in the basketball game."

There are times when voyeurism and exhibitionism are not necessarily pathological forms of behavior. In the case of Evelyn, a little nudity went a long way. It sent a direct message to her husband— one he'll probably never forget. It reminded him that she was there. Sometimes we have to jolt people's senses to remind them that sex is an option.

"James" tells a different tale.

"I've been married three years, but I still get a kick out of seeing Lucy without a stitch on. I especially like looking at her when she doesn't know I'm looking. Sometimes when she's asleep after we've screwed around, I pull the covers off her and stare in awe at her beautiful body. Sometimes I fiddle with myself and come a second time. Then if she stirs and wakes up, and notices me watching her, we end up fucking again."

Who can deny that the visual aspects of sex are highly stimulating. And they should not be downplayed, underrated, or ignored. Sex appeal, to a large degree, is based on looks. Take advantage of this natural plus in sex.

"Yolanda," a beautician, confided to me that "the sexiest part of sex for me is when I take off my boyfriend's underpants. Slowly, *very* slowly, I start to pull them down, feeling the hardness of him start to grow. I love the way it looks when his buttocks are bared. I love the look of his pubic hair—a thin line of black against his dark brown skin, and the stark white of his Calvin Klein briefs. Then when I get them down around his knees, I go berserk and rip them off."

Play erotic games like hide-and-go-seek nude. In college, my friends and I used to play strip poker, but eventually we graduated to Strip Monopoly, Strip Scrabble, and Strip Twister. I belonged to a singing group called "The Society Of Orpheus And Bacchus (The SOBs)" and we used to do everything from playing volleyball to driving long distances in the buff. Once at Mount Vernon Women's College in Washington, D.C., we even performed a concert in our birthday suits. We were severely castigated by the school authorities, but the girls gave us a standing ovation.

MOUTHING OFF

Perhaps the most underappreciated erogenous zone is the mouth. I can hear you saying, "But I use my mouth all the time!" Of course, you do. So do I. Gladly. But I'm speaking of those times when the oral cavity is being used as a vehicle of erotic expression, not as a sexual orifice. Talking about sex while making love adds a new dimension to the experience. Just the act of letting out your sexual feelings via the throat canal can be viscerally arousing. It is a fantasy of a verbal order. Let's listen in on some of these playful diversions:

BEDROOM VOICES

Vulgarity is in the ears of the beholder. Sometimes bedroom conversations are more compelling if you lower the tone of your voice. Experiment with different timbres. Other languages. I know one man who made a point of riding the bus each Sunday in Chinatown because he loved the sound of the women's voices. When you're making love, why not try words that are lustier, throatier, heartier. More active, less analysed. Instead of saying, "I'm horny," try saying, "Right now, I want to rub my hands all over your gorgeous body." Instead of saying, "You do what you want, I'm tired," why not say, "Sit on top of me and focus all your attention on yourself. It would really turn me on if you take command, and I just watch. Pretend I'm behind bars and you can't reach me!"

Nor for that matter is there any reason to curtail verbalizing your sexual desires and fantasies. As long as you're not screaming so loud that you disturb your neighbors, let your filthy imagination have the floor. Talk dirty—give details about how good it feels, why you like it, where you like it. Put your heart and soul into it.

Growl out a few scandalous expressions. You may want to practice them now. Find the words that really get *you* going. Find the flavor of the phrase in the way it comes out of your mouth. "Cassandra" had her own idiosyncratic way of sexually verbalizing. At the brink of orgasm she would lapse into a shouting mode— "Fuck, shit! Fuck, shit! Fuck, shit!" she would cry out. It sounds fairly coarse on paper, but in the throes of a cataclysmic climax, it had its charm.

Even though it may not be politically correct, or fashionable, it can sometimes be amusing to call each other by nasty names, like shrew, harlot, nympho. Or bastard, brute, or bruiser. Epithets like these work well if the joke is shared. You can also vent spleen by cursing your mate at the moment of orgasm. Take on different personalities. Call him sir, and ask him to call you madam. The only time I think you're asking for trouble during sexual verbalizing is if you holler out somebody's else's name other than your partner's when you come. Relationships have rarely survived such errors in judgment.

BEDTIME STORIES

Telling sexy stories ("narratophilia") is another variation of sexual fantasy that is virtually an art form. "Elsa" is one coquette who considers herself the Isak Dinesen of the boudoir. She starts up a tale with a tiny anecdote and before you know it you are completely engrossed in a blistering lusty intrigue of epic proportions. Her favorite kick is to tell her "first-time" story whenever she makes love to a new man. She tells about how she lost her "cherry" to a second cousin twice removed on a farm in the Appalachian mountains. She expresses herself with great candor, but also with an endearing, self-effacing wit. Explaining how she felt having sex for the first time as a young "wood nymph," she brings her current lover into the amorous reverie with her. She could be making the whole thing up. But does it matter? What counts is that she succeeds in creating a colorful backdrop to sex.

HOT READS

For those of you who don't have Elsa's spontaneous imagination or are too shy to invent or recount your own Rabelasian adventures, I suggest reading previously written erotica aloud. This is an area of sexual stimulation that is rarely discussed, except by other practitioners to each other. There are hundreds of magazines on the market that feature steamy stories told in the first person. Or go to your local library and take out *Delta Of Venus* by Anaïs Nin. Or read James Joyce's personal letters. Find the subject matter that gets you all hot and bothered. Read it to your sex mate—no holds barred. In turn, you may find out what turns him on as you observe him reacting physically to the tale.

It may excite you to read a bedtime fable to your partner as he or she performs oral sex on you. You may never get to the end of the tale, but you've had a different and diverting experience along the way.

Finally, you may wish to write your own sexual fantasies on paper and read them to your partner or let her read them to you. Such self-exploration (as witnessed in writing your Sex Bio) can only increase the intimacy and camaraderie Terrific Sex has to offer.

THE SILENT TREATMENT

As with any good rule, there is bound to be an exception that proves its worth. The exception here is the time that you choose to remain absolutely, totally silent.

"Wally and Amelia" made love once in complete silence. They had to. The cosmopolitan couple were traveling behind the Iron Curtain, and they thought their room was bugged. "You can't get a double bed in Russia," Amelia explains. "Socialist countries are very puritanical. And as an émigré, I was considered an enemy of the state. I knew our conversations were being tape-recorded. It was very disturbing."

Wally explains, "The walls were so thin, we had to make sure no one heard us doing it. The problem in the Soviet Union is that they don't want people to get close and intimate with each other in bed. That's when a lot of intense sharing goes on."

What the couple discovered is that by making love without making a sound, they added a dimension of intrigue and breathless secrecy to their sex life that was very gratifying. "I was surprised how responsive my body became to his touches, as if every nerve ending had been isolated and exposed. Not talking, not even whispering, made everything so intense. Just remembering how it felt gives me goose pimples now." Wally adds, "Trying to keep your mouth shut while coming

196

was a new experience. At one point, Amelia cupped her hand over my mouth 'cause it looked like I was ready to scream.''

You can try similar espionage-esque touches by wearing gags, covering each other's mouths with your hands, or merely by biting your lip and keeping silent. If the sex is good, it will be very hard to keep your trap shut. But that's what makes it such a challenge. The more difficult it gets, the more you just want to announce to the world how great it feels!

THE PIZZAZZ OF PHONE SEX

Before the AIDS crisis I don't think I'd ever heard of Phone Sex. I'd certainly heard of the obscene phone call. I'd received a few of my own. I'd heard of phone numbers you could call and hear a recording of a woman telling obscene jokes over the line. Usually, it wasn't worth the dime it then cost to call. Once, I even saw a film in which a woman made love to herself *with* a phone. Yet, over the last five years, a whole new phenomenon has developed in which men and women, married or single, gay or straight, alone or in pairs are getting off on the phone.

Open any erotic magazine today and you're instantly bombarded with advertisements for "Phone Sex," "Dial A Stud!", "Hooker Hotline!", "Hunk On Hold," "Talk Dirty To Me!", "Muscles Mania." Just listen to the hit song "Making Love On The Phone"— and you can't help but reach out and touch someone.

There are essentially two brands of phone sex. The

first entails answering one of these telephone services. These can be expensive—thirty to fifty bucks a pop—and you're dealing with a stranger. It's easy, quick, and efficient.

The other type of phone sex involves hooking up with someone for free. This has been accomplished by dialing an absolute stranger. (The infamous obscene phone call, which is illegal, accounts for some twenty thousand complaints a year in metropolitan New York alone!) You should try connecting with a date or, if you're married, your spouse. Many married couples enjoy engaging in phone sex while one of them is off on business, or away for the weekend. Here the experiences of "Bedroom Voices" and "Bedtime Stories" can come in very handy. Don't be bashful about exposing your innermost fantasies on the phone. Dial S For Sex and be on your way!

LIGHTS, CAMERA, ACTION!

A novel way to spice up your sex life is to rent or buy your own video equipment and make your own "dirty movies." It's not as hard as it sounds.

"Michael," an architect from Manhattan, tried it and loved it.

"Catherine was going away for a two-week business trip and I wanted something to look at while she was gone. We rented a video camera from the local videostore and bought a couple of video tapes. That night I filmed her at dinner, around the living room, and eventually in bed. It was her idea to leave the camera running on a tripod while we fucked. I would never have thought of it. Knowing that the camera was rolling while we were going at it was great. I found myself acting out a lot of my fantasies, being more aggressive, giving her orders, telling her what it felt like. Knowing that our voices were being taped added to the excitement. I got more vocal—and when I came I really put on a show. Later, of course, we looked at the tape and neither of us could believe how incredible it was. We looked pretty good, too. I think it's better than any porn film I've ever seen. I'm not sure which I liked more. Watching it, or making it."

Catherine had her own observations.

"Michael thought I was joking. But I wasn't. I really wanted to see what we looked like making love. I was surprised when I saw it, because I'd never seen Michael from the back before. I couldn't get over the way his buns looked moving up and down. Wow! He was fucking me so fast and hard, it was amazing. Next time I'm going to get on top and be the star."

Why not film each other in the bathtub or shower and watch it next time during foreplay. Or film each other masturbating. As you're being photographed, make love to the camera, talk to your partner about what you'd like to do to her or him. Get into it. You don't have to be Sir Laurence Olivier or Meryl Streep to perform well. The method that works best is just to be yourself.

LITE S&M

A little bondage and humiliation can be a lot of fun!

S&M is short for sadomasochism, a combined term that has traditionally been used to describe the giving and receiving of pain for erotic gratification. The reason the terms are combined is because it's very hard to be a sadist without a masochist around—and vice versa. Usually, they're different aspects of the same person. As far as Terrific Sex goes, I prefer to use the expression Lite S&M to describe those voluntary activities shared by two loving, caring sex partners. Especially now that the threat of AIDS has caused us all to look at the limitations of sex, Lite S&M can be very practical in creating a highly charged sexual atmosphere, as well as igniting deep-seated, fascinating erotic fantasies.

Although they love to tumble, the average Jack and Jill is more or less reticent about talking about S&M, but we all do experience some aspect of this pleasure every day of our lives. One enthusiast has suggested that "to ignore sadomasochism . . . is to ignore life itself."

Kinsey found that one in eight females and one in five males were aroused by sadomasochistic stories. One need only read any of the historical romances bulging out of the racks in drug stores to realize that forceful lovemaking, a little roughhousing, and general horsing around have enormous appeal to the general public. On a more sophisticated plane, the success of

Helmut Newton's photograph albums also attest to this truth about our society.

S&M also has implications in the psychology of sex, how we perceive eroticism in others and ourselves. Juliette, the authoress of *The Autobiography Of A Dominatrix*, has written, "Sometimes, thinking about a perverted act can be much more exciting than the act itself." And Toni Rose, contributing to the same collection of essays on sadomasochism has stated that "for some it's the fear of the whip, not the actual whipping that gets them. They get off on what they think I'm going to do."

The woman who fantasizes about being "taken" against her will by a big brute of a man (the "Blanche Dubois Complex") is indulging in a minor S&M scenario. The man who dreams about a chambermaid flogging his buttocks with a wet towel is probably a masochist. The lady who imagines tying up her husband for three hours while she licks his entire body from head to toe, and back again, is undoubtedly a sadist, a rather remarkable one at that, but she's also lightly dusted with masochistic predilections. You don't have to actually perform these acts to be a contender. What matters is how such ideas or images effect you sexually. They can be a real boost to your bedroom antics.

The whole secret to the allure of S&M in its lighter forms is the lessening of alternatives. It's not removing one's clothes that makes S&M so erotic, it's removing one's options. If you're hands are tied, you can't be concerned with touching or stroking your friend. Therefore, you concentrate more fully on the remaining choices and sensations. For instance, if you are restrained on a bed, hands tied with silk scarves to the bedposts, and your partner is running a tiny little paintbrush up and down your skin, the pleasure is going to be all that much greater because it is contained. You are not at liberty to shake him off. Letting go of one's own control is the essence of bondage. Many lovers of Lite S&M claim that the orgasms experienced under such limitations are often superior, more intense than those experienced in so-called normal sex.

"Nick," a computer analyst, doubles at night as a director of S&M scenarios. He and his girlfriend get off on creating scenes. One time he wrapped her up completely in ace bandages. She liked feeling totally in his power. These two shared a great deal of trust. It would be foolish to enact such scenes with a stranger or someone you couldn't be sure of.

In this regard, many Lite S&M activities resemble the "trust test" performed at camps and in group therapy where you fall back, blindfolded, into the waiting arms of a friend. For some of us, it takes longer to let go. But being able to trust is a healthy experience. Being bound or gagged adds a *frisson* to the sexual pleasure.

"James," a thirty-two-year-old actor, related to me how he often likes to have his hands and legs restrained while indulging in foreplay. "It started a few years back when I broke my leg skiing. My girlfriend got tired of waiting for the cast to come off and one night she 'raped me.' She was the aggressor. Because of my leg, I couldn't get up or move away. She had total control. Something about the sex was extra-special that night. Having her go down on me in that helpless state was totally incredible. Now, I've got a new girlfriend but I've shown her how to seduce me by tying my legs together with one of my ties. Then she starts to kiss me all over from the legs up to my shoulders. Since I can't get up and pounce on her, all my feelings go crazy in my groin. I feel like I want to explode! She's explode! She's keen to it, and pretty soon she slides on top of me and starts to fuck me mercilessly. Oh, man, I'm telling you, you've never felt anything so good."

"Jennifer" found her own way of adding a new dimension to her lovemaking. "I'm a big one for being the boss at my job," she says of her work as a singing coach. "But when I'm with my man I like to be told what to do. And the way I like to do it, is blind as a bat. I bought this hood and when my boyfriend tells me to put it on, I do. Once I can't see anything, I start to see so much more. Wild things in my mind. I invent surroundings. I imagine that I'm in the middle of a large table in a huge Gothic hall. My boyfriend makes me kiss his boots. He grabs me by the hair and commands me to suck his dick. That always makes me feel fantastic. I do just as he tells me to. Then he makes me lie down while he licks my nipples and plays with my pussy. When he fucks me, it's different each time because I can't see him. I can only feel the bigness and hardness of him. My whole body comes alive, responding to his every touch! I feel like I'm on fire!"

These three people have touched upon various aspects of Lite S&M and playful lovemaking. But there are many other variations, from spanking and humiliation, to walking on someone's back while wearing stiletto heels, not to mention the eternal charm of handcuffs.

Take a trip to your local adult novelty shop—the Pink Pussycat Boutique near you. Expose yourself to the wealth of imaginative offerings there. Some will undoubtedly appall you, but maybe you'll find the special gadget—a body harness, a tit clamp, a bullwhip—that has *you* written all over it.

POST SCRIPT

WHEN TOMORROW COMES

THE FUTURE
OF SEX

I'm sorry to say that our bawdy romp through the sometimes serious, sometimes exhausting, but always entertaining fifteen Terrific Sex Pleasure Principles has come to a close. I haven't run out of things to tell you. In fact, there's so much I haven't covered. But time calls, and I want to get this book out to you as soon as possible. Of course there are thousands of other equally amusing, rewarding, mind-blowing experiences yet to be explored. No doubt some are even superior. Good. They're out there. Now that you know the ground rules, go out and discover them for yourself. And let me know how you've fared.

I also hope having read this book, you'll recognize how important it is to all of us, both personally and together, to take these initiatives—to spread the word that sex is here to stay, better than ever. There are no reasons to listen to those nay-sayers who insist we go back to eating graham crackers, drinking warm milk to stem our sexual desires, strapping on moral chastity belts, all the while turning our backs on our natural instincts and passions. Just think of the fun they're missing. Today, you can embrace your erotic personality as an intrinsic and wonderful extension of yourself.

If, as Dr. Mathilde Krim and other experts optimistically speculate, modern science will one day triumph over the deadly disease of AIDS that has swept into our lives and knocked the wind out of our sails, taking with it so many talented, young and courageous people, then hopefully we'll be able to return wholeheartedly to the less restrictive practices of yesteryear. We'll be older perhaps, but certainly much wiser. Think how much more we'll appreciate good sex. And how much more knowledge, expertise, and experience we can bring to it. The good news is and forever can be that by engaging in Terrific Sex we can rise above our fears and trepidations and prevent tragedy. We can take charge of our lives and make the most of our future.

No matter what the outcome, Terrific Sex is something you and I can always look forward to.

Good luck!